Teacher's Resource Blackline Masters

CONTENTS

Newsletters

Dear Family,

WELCOME...to the new school year.

I'd like to invite you to join me in making this an exciting and rewarding year for your child. One of the things I'll be asking you to do is share information that will help me get to know your child better.

Throughout the year, I'll be sending home ideas for activities that you can do with your child to reinforce what we're learning in school. Please become involved as much as you can. Studies have shown that children who get support at home in reading and learning do better in school.

Here are two suggestions for things to do at home:

- **Read and discuss books with your child.** Even after children have learned to read on their own, there are many benefits to reading aloud to your child—and to letting your child read to you. Visit the library together so you can choose books that both of you will enjoy.

- **Let your child see *you* reading.** It's important to show your child that you think reading is valuable and enjoyable.

One other thing: I always appreciate having adult volunteers assist with classroom activities. If you can give some time in the classroom or at home with preparation, please let me know.

Thanks for working with me as a partner in your child's education. Together, we can help your child have a successful year!

Sincerely,

_____

Estimada familia:

¡Bienvenidos al nuevo año escolar!

Mi deseo es que juntos podamos hacer de éste un año productivo y divertido. Una de las cosas que les voy a pedir es que compartan conmigo información acerca de su niño o niña. Esa información me ayudará a conocer mejor a los niños.

Durante el año escolar, les enviaré cartas con ideas de actividades que pueden hacer juntos en casa. Esas actividades ayudarán a complementar lo que aprendemos en clase. Por favor, colaboren tanto como puedan. Estudios han demostrado que los niños que reciben apoyo en sus casas siguen mejor en la escuela.

A continuación hay dos sugerencias importantes de actividades que pueden hacer en casa:

- **Lean libros juntos y hablen de lo que leen.** Aunque los niños ya sepan leer, es muy beneficioso que usted les lea en voz alta y también que ellos lean voz alta para los demás. Vayan a la biblioteca y escojan libros que les gusten a ambos.

- **Asegúrense de que su niño o niña lo vea leer a usted.** Es importante que usted demuestre que la lectura es importante y divertida.

Otra cosa importante: Yo siempre aprecio la ayuda que puedan prestar voluntarios adultos con las actividades de la clase. Por favor, avísenme si me pueden ayudar en el salón de clases, o en su casa, con detalles relacionados a la preparación de actividades.

Les agradezco de antemano por participar en la educación de su niño o niña. Juntos podemos ayudarle a tener un año muy exitoso.

Atentamente,

_____

Newsletter

Dear Family,

For the next few weeks, we will be enjoying the theme *Off to Adventure!* Your child will read exciting stories about real-life and fantasy adventures.

Off to Adventure!

Theme-Related Activities to Do Together

In Search of Adventure

Take your child to the library and explore ways to find adventure stories. Try key words, such as *adventure, mountains,* or *blizzards* in the computer or card catalog. Ask a librarian for the names of authors who write adventure stories.

Leave-No-Trace Picnic

Plan a leave-no-trace picnic with your child with the goal of leaving no evidence of your presence when you leave the picnic site. Together decide on the menu and your plans for taking away your trash. Have your child help shop for and prepare the food.

Adventures Then and Now

Have your child listen with eyes shut as you describe an adventure from your childhood. Sketch part of the adventure as you tell the story. When you finish, have your child say which part the sketch illustrates. Then challenge your child to switch roles and be the storyteller and illustrator.

Theme-Related Books to Enjoy Together!

The Great Pig Escape *by Eileen Christelow. Houghton 1996 (32p) paper* The pigs that Bert and Ethel are taking to market have a better idea.

The Secret Shortcut *by Mark Teague. Scholastic 1996 (32p); also paper* Wendell and Floyd, who can't seem to get to school on time, think they've finally found the answer.

Madeline *by Ludwig Bemelmans. Viking 1958; also paper* The adventures of the Paris orphan have remained popular since 1939. Also available in Spanish.

The Adventures of Sparrowboy *by Brian Pinkney. Simon 1997 (32p)* Henry the paperboy suddenly finds that he is a flying superhero, just like his comic strip idol.

Brave Irene *by William Steig. Farrar 1986 (32p); also paper* Irene braves a snowstorm to deliver a new gown to the duchess. Available in Spanish as *Irene, la valiente.*

Amelia and Eleanor Go for a Ride *by Pam Munoz Ryan. Scholastic 1999 (32p)* Amelia Earhart and Eleanor Roosevelt leave a White House dinner and take a plane ride.

Boletín

Estimada familia:

Durante las próximas semanas, vamos a tratar el tema *¡A la aventura!* Su niño o niña va a leer historias entretenidas acerca de aventuras reales y de fantasía.

¡A la aventura!

Actividades para hacer juntos

En busca de aventuras

Vayan juntos a la biblioteca y busquen historias de aventuras. Busquen en la computadora o en el fichero, usando palabras clave, tales como: *aventura*, *montañas* o *tormentas*. Pidan a la bibliotecaria nombres de autores de historias de aventuras.

Como si nadie hubiera estado

Organicen una merienda afuera, en la que se aseguren de no dejar señal de que han estado en ese lugar. Decidan lo que comerán y hagan planes para deshacerse de la basura. Pida a su niño o niña que le ayude a comprar y a preparar la comida.

Aventuras de ayer y hoy

Pida a su niño o niña que escuche con los ojos cerrados, mientras usted describe una aventura de su propia niñez. Mientras cuenta, haga un dibujo de una parte de la aventura. Después, pida a su niño o niña que le diga qué parte de la historia ilustró usted.

Libros relacionados al tema que pueden leer juntos

The Great Pig Escape *por Eileen Christelow. Houghton 1996 (32pp) libro de bolsillo* Los cerditos que Bert y Ethel llevan al mercado tienen un plan mejor.

The Secret Shortcut *por Mark Teague. Scholastic 1996 (32pp); también libro de bolsillo* Wendell y Floyd, quienes no pueden llegar a tiempo a la escuela, creen haber hallado la solución.

Madeline *por Ludwig Bemelmans. Viking 1958; también libro de bolsillo* Las aventuras de la huérfana parisiana han sido populares desde 1939. Disponible en español.

The Adventures of Sparrowboy *por Brian Pinkney. Simon 1997 (32pp)* Henry, el niño que reparte los periódicos, de repente se transforma en superhéroe volador.

Brave Irene *por William Steig. Farrar 1986 (32pp); también libro de bolsillo* Irene enfrenta una tormenta de nieve para llevar un nuevo traje a la duquesa. Disponible en español con el título *Irene, la valiente.*

Amelia and Eleanor Go for a Ride *por Pam Muñoz Ryan. Scholastic 1999 (32pp)* Amelia Earhart y Eleanor Roosevelt salen de la Casa Blanca para dar una vuelta en avión.

Newsletter

Dear Family,

For the next few weeks, our class will be reading the theme *Celebrating Traditions*. Your child will explore ways people across the United States celebrate family and cultural traditions and how these traditions enrich their lives.

Celebrating Traditions

Theme-Related Activities to Do Together

Designer You

Have your child list several visual symbols for things he or she enjoys (for example, a soccer ball if he or she plays soccer). Then help your child plan a square for a cloth quilt or a collage that includes these symbols.

Prisms and Rainbows

Help your child research prisms and write several sentences that explain how light passing through a prism can create a rainbow. Then have your child explain in his or her own words how a prism can "make" a rainbow.

Music and Dance

Together with your child look for videos or audio tapes with music from various cultures. Listen to the tapes together and identify the subject of the music. Is it celebratory? Does it tell a story?

Theme-Related Books to Enjoy Together!

The Wedding by *Angela Johnson. Orchard 1999 (32p)* Daisy is both glad and sorry that her older sister is getting married.

A Picnic in October by *Eve Bunting. Harcourt 1999 (32p)* Tony finally understands why his grandmother wants to celebrate her birthday every year at the Statue of Liberty.

Song of Shiprock Fair by *Luci Tapahonso. Kiva 1999 (32p)* Nezbah, a young Navajo girl, relates her family's experiences at the Navajo Nation's Annual Shiprock Fair.

Seven Candles for Kwanzaa by *Andrea Davis Pinkney. Dial 1993 (32p); also paper* A family celebrates the seven-day festival of Kwanzaa.

Moon Festival by *Ching Yeung Russell. Boyds Mills 1997 (32p)* The author recalls celebrating the traditional Moon Festival when she was a child in China.

Daughter's Day Blues by *Laura Pegram. Dial 2000 (32p)* Because her little brother gets so much attention, Phyllis Mae is delighted when her mother and grandmother decide to celebrate Daughter's Day.

Boletín

Estimada familia:

Durante las próximas semanas, el tema de nuestra lectura será *Celebremos las tradiciones*. Su niño o niña aprenderá las formas en que las personas a través de los Estados Unidos celebran ricas tradiciones familiares y culturales.

Celebremos las tradiciones

Actividades para hacer juntos

A diseñar

Pida a su niño o niña que nombre varios símbolos visuales para lo que a él o a ella le gusta hacer (por ejemplo: un balón de fútbol, si juega al fútbol). Luego ayúdele a diseñar un cuadrado de tela para una colcha o un montaje que incluya esos símbolos.

Los prismas y el arco iris

Ayude a su niño o niña a investigar los prismas y a escribir varias oraciones que expliquen cómo la luz que pasa a través de un prisma forma un arco iris. Luego pídale que explique cómo un prisma "forma" un arco iris.

Música y baile

Con su niño o niña, busquen vídeos o cintas de audio con música de varias culturas. Miren y escuchen juntos los vídeos o cintas e identifiquen el tema de la música. ¿Es una celebración? ¿Relata una historia?

Libros relacionados al tema que pueden leer juntos

The Wedding *por Angela Johnson. Orchard 1999 (32pp)* Daisy se siente contenta y triste al mismo tiempo, porque su hermana mayor se casa.

A Picnic in October *por Eve Bunting. Harcourt 1999 (32pp)* Tony por fin entiende por qué su abuela quiere celebrar su cumpleaños todos los años en la Estatua de la libertad.

Song of Shiprock Fair *por Luci Tapahonso. Kiva 1999 (32pp)* Nezbah, una muchacha navajo, cuenta las experiencias de su familia en la feria anual Shiprock de los navajo.

Seven Candles for Kwanzaa *por Andrea Davis Pinkney. Dial 1993 (32pp); también libro de bolsillo* Una familia celebra el festival de siete días de Kwanzaa.

Moon Festival *por Ching Yeung Russell. Boyds Mills 1997 (32pp)* La autora recuerda cuando de niña celebraba en China el tradicional Festival de la luna.

Daughter's Day Blues *por Laura Pegram. Dial 2000 (32pp)* Debido a que su hermano menor recibe tanta atención, Phyllis Mae se siente dichosa cuando su propia madre y abuela deciden celebrar el Día de las hijas.

Newsletter

Incredible Stories

Dear Family,

For the next few weeks, our class will be having fun with the theme *Incredible Stories*. From a gentle giant who defends a town to a giant creature that invades a city, the fantasy stories in this theme will amaze your child.

Theme-Related Activities to Do Together

Size Comparisons

Help your child research and list the weights of family pets and siblings. Help him or her list these in rank order from the greatest to the least. Then ask the following: Who on the list weighs the most? The least? More or less than another child or pet?

Neighborhood Tale

Have your child invent an incredible character, such as an animal that talks or someone who has action-figure power and strength. Then take a walk together and discuss the incredible adventures the character could have in your neighborhood.

Fantasy Animal

With your child, create a fantasy creature by combining pictures from old magazines. For example, put the head of an elephant on the body of an ostrich with the tail from an iguana. Give the creature a funny name.

Theme-Related Books to Enjoy Together!

The Best Place *by Susan Meddaugh. Houghton 1999 (32p)* A wolf who loves his screened-in porch suddenly wonders if it really is the best place in the world.

Jumanji *by Chris Van Allsburg. Houghton 1981 (32p)* Two children get more than they bargained for in a mysterious jungle-adventure board game. Also available in Spanish.

The True Story of the Three Little Pigs! *by Jon Scieszka. Viking 1989 (32p); also paper* A. Wolf, claiming he was framed, wants to set the record straight. Available in Spanish as *La verdadera historia de los tres cerditos.*

Martha Blah Blah *by Susan Meddaugh. Houghton 1996 (32p); also paper* When Martha the dog starts losing her ability to speak, drastic measures are called for.

Cloudy with a Chance of Meatballs *by Judi Barrett. Atheneum 1978 (32p)* Delicious food rains from the sky in the town of Chewandswallow, but then disaster strikes.

A Day with Wilbur Robinson *by William Joyce. Harper 1990 (32p); also paper* A visitor finds that a day at Wilbur Robinson's house is filled with strange and wonderful adventures.

Boletín

Cuentos fantásticos

Estimada familia:

Durante las próximas semanas, nuestra clase tratará el tema *Cuentos fantásticos*. Estas historias de fantasía le encantarán a su niño o niña, desde el gigante gentil que defiende una ciudad, hasta la criatura gigante que invade una ciudad.

Actividades para hacer juntos

Comparación de tamaños

Ayude a su niño o niña a hacer una lista del peso de sus hermanos y hermanas, y de las mascotas que tengan en casa. Ayúdele a ordenar los pesos, del más pesado al menos pesado. Luego pregúntele: ¿Quién pesa más según la lista? ¿Quién pesa menos?

Cuento del vecindario

Pida a su niño o niña que invente un personaje fantástico, como un animal que hable o alguien que tenga poderes extraordinarios. Luego vayan de paseo y hablen de las increíbles aventuras que tendría este personaje por su vecindario.

Animal fantástico

Combinen ilustraciones de revistas viejas para crear con su niño o niña una criatura de fantasía. Por ejemplo, junten la cabeza de un elefante con el cuerpo de un avestruz y la cola de una iguana. Den a la criatura un nombre cómico.

Libros relacionados al tema que pueden leer juntos

The Best Place *por Susan Meddaugh. Houghton 1999 (32pp)* Un lobo, encantado con su terraza cubierta, se pregunta si ese es de veras el mejor lugar del mundo.

Jumanji *por Chris Van Allsburg. Houghton 1981 (32pp)* Dos niños viven más de lo esperado en este misterioso juego de aventura en la selva. Disponible en español.

The True History of the Three Little Pigs! *por Jon Scieszka. Viking 1989 (32pp); también libro de bolsillo* A. Lobo quiere rectificar la versión tradicional de lo que sucedió en esta historia, sosteniendo que lo trata injustamente. Disponible en español con el título *La verdadera historia de los tres cerditos.*

Martha Blah Blah *por Susan Meddaugh. Houghton 1996 (32pp); también libro de bolsillo* Cuando Martha comienza a perder su capacidad de hablar, hay que tomar medidas drásticas.

Cloudy with a Chance of Meatballs *por Judi Barrett. Atheneum 1978 (32pp)* Comida deliciosa llueve del cielo en el pueblo de Chewandswallow, pero luego ocurre un desastre.

A Day with Wilbur Robinson *por William Joyce. Harper 1990 (32pp); también libro de bolsillo* Un visitante descubre que pasar un día en la casa de Wilbur Robinson implica aventuras extrañas y maravillosas.

Newsletter

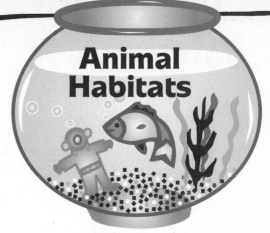

Animal Habitats

Dear Family,

For the next few weeks, we will be exploring the theme *Animal Habitats*. As we learn about places where animals live, we will discover some ways in which people and animals interact.

Theme-Related Activities to Do Together

State Symbols
Help your child research your state's bird or animal. Then encourage him or her to write sentences that describe this state symbol.

Bird Count
Count with your child the different birds you see over one weekend. List the names of birds that you recognize. Use a field guide to help you identify birds you do not know.

Working with Animals
There are many jobs that involve working with animals. Have your child select one such job. Then together research the different kinds of tasks the job entails and the training needed to do the job.

Theme-Related Books to Enjoy Together!

Where Are the Night Animals? *by Mary Ann Fraser. Harper 1999 (32p)* Bats, tree frogs, barn owls, and raccoons are just a few of the nocturnal animals introduced to young readers.

Urban Roosts *by Barbara Bash. Little Brown 1992 (32p); also paper* In recent years thirteen bird species have made their homes in the heart of large cities.

A Beach for the Birds *by Bruce McMillan. Houghton 1993 (32p)* Humans and the endangered Least Tern coexist on the beaches of Maine.

Seashore Babies *by Kathy Darling. Walker 1997 (32p)* Featured are young animals that live along the seashore, including crabs, dolphins, and terns. See others in this series.

Tracks in the Wild *by Betsy Bowen. Houghton 1998 (32p)* The author introduces readers to thirteen animals found in the woods near her Minnesota home.

Watching Desert Wildlife *by Jim Arnosky. National Geographic 1998 (32p)* Naturalist Arnosky describes the animal life found on the Chihuahuan and Sonoran deserts in America's Southwest.

Boletín

Animales en su hábitat

Estimada familia:

Durante las próximas semanas, vamos a explorar el tema *Animales en su hábitat*. Al aprender de los lugares donde viven los animales, vamos a descubrir algunas maneras en que se relacionan las personas y los animales.

Actividades para hacer juntos

Símbolos estatales

Ayude a su niño o niña a investigar el ave o el animal que representa al estado donde ustedes residen. Luego anímelo a escribir una descripción de este símbolo.

Conteo de aves

Cuente con su niño o niña las distintas aves que vean durante un fin de semana. Hagan una lista de los nombres de las aves que reconozcan. Usen una guía de aves para identificar las que no conozcan.

Trabajando con los animales

Hay muchos trabajos en los que se trabaja con animales. Pida a su niño o niña que seleccione uno de esos trabajos. Luego investiguen juntos las tareas y el entrenamiento que requiere ese trabajo.

Libros relacionados al tema que pueden leer juntos

Where Are the Night Animals? *por Mary Ann Fraser. Harper 1999 (32pp)* Murciélagos, ranas arbóreas, lechuzas bodegueras y mapaches, son algunos de los animales nocturnos que se presentan aquí.

Urban Roosts *por Barbara Bash. Little Brown 1992 (32pp); también libro de bolsillo* En años recientes, trece especies de aves se han establecido en el corazón de las grandes ciudades.

A Beach for the Birds *por Bruce McMillan. Houghton 1993 (32pp)* Los seres humanos y los gaviotines (aves en vía de extinción) coexisten en las playas de Maine.

Seashore Babies *por Kathy Darling. Walker 1997 (32pp)* Esta es una selección sobre animales que viven en las playas, incluyendo las crías de cangrejos, delfines y golondrinas. Vean otros libros de la serie.

Tracks in the Wild *por Betsy Bowen. Houghton 1998 (32pp)* La autora presenta a los lectores trece animales de los bosques que quedan cerca de su casa en Minnesota.

Watching Desert Wildlife *por Jim Arnosky. National Geographic 1998 (32pp)* El naturalista Arnosky describe la vida animal en los desiertos de Chihuahua y Sonora en el suroeste de los Estados Unidos.

Newsletter

Voyagers

Dear Family,

For the next few weeks, we will be taking off with the theme *Voyagers*. We'll learn about courageous explorers and historic journeys, such as Sir Ernest Shackleton's epic adventure in Antarctica.

Theme-Related Activities to Do Together

Tracing Voyages
Challenge your child to pick a story that has a voyager in it and trace on a map or globe the path the voyager took.

Current Expeditions
Along with your child listen to the news on radio or TV or look through newspapers or magazines to find stories about modern-day explorers.

Video Voyage
Help your child select a video about an explorer or a voyage into new surroundings. Watch it together and share what you enjoy the most in the film.

Theme-Related Books to Enjoy Together!

The Sailor's Alphabet *by Michael McCurdy. Houghton 1998 (32p)* This collection of sea chanteys sung by sailors in the 1880s also includes a tour of a typical United State Navy frigate of that time.

Annushka's Voyage *by Edith Tarbescu. Clarion 1998 (32p)* When Annushka and Tanya get word from their father in America, they sail from Russia to be reunited with him at Ellis Island.

Spray *by Robert Blake. Penguin 1996 (32p)* The true story of Captain Joshua Slocum is woven into this story of a lonely boy.

Good-bye for Today *by Peter and Connie Roop. Atheneum 2000 (48p)* A young girl keeps a journal as she sails with her family from Japan to the Arctic aboard a whaling ship captained by her father.

How Many Days to America? *by Eve Bunting. Houghton 1990 (32p)* A family forced off its Caribbean island sets sail for America in a small fishing boat.

If You Sailed on the Mayflower *by Ann McGovern. Scholastic 1991 (80p); also paper* This book answers many questions about Pilgrim life, both on board ship and on shore.

Boletín

Jornadas

Estimada familia:

Durante las próximas semanas, vamos a tratar el tema *Jornadas*. Aprenderemos acerca de exploradores valientes y de viajes históricos, como las épicas aventuras de Sir Ernest Shackleton en la Antártida.

Actividades para hacer juntos

Trazando viajes

Pida a su niño o niña que escoja la historia de un explorador, y que trace la ruta de su viaje en un mapa o en un globo terráqueo.

Expediciones de hoy en día

Escuchen juntos las noticias en la radio o en la televisión, o lean diarios o revistas, para hallar historias acerca de exploradores de hoy en día.

Viaje en vídeo

Ayude a su niño o niña a seleccionar un vídeo acerca de un explorador o acerca de un viaje a lugares inexplorados. Vean el vídeo juntos y hablen de lo que disfrutaron más.

Libros relacionados al tema que pueden leer juntos

The Sailor's Alphabet *por Michael McCurdy. Houghton 1998 (32pp)* Esta colección de salomas, cantadas por marineros en la década de 1880, incluye una excursión en una fragata típica de ese período.

Annushka's Voyage *por Edith Tarbescu. Clarion 1998 (32pp)* Apenas Annushka y Tanya oyen noticias de su padre en los Estados Unidos, toman un barco desde Rusia, para reunirse con él en Ellis Island.

Spray *por Robert Blake. Penguin 1996 (32pp)* La verdadera historia del capitán Joshua Slocum forma parte de la historia de un joven solitario.

Good-bye for Today *por Peter y Connie Roop. Atheneum 2000 (48pp)* Una niña escribe en su diario mientras viaja con su familia desde Japón hasta el Ártico en un barco ballenero bajo el mando de su padre.

How Many Days to America? *por Eve Bunting. Houghton 1990 (32pp)* Una familia forzada a abandonar su isla en el Caribe se embarca en un bote de pesca hacia los Estados Unidos.

If You Sailed on the Mayflower *por Ann McGovern. Scholastic 1991 (80pp); también libro de bolsillo* Este libro contesta muchas preguntas acerca de la vida de los peregrinos, tanto en sus viajes en barco como en tierra firme.

Newsletter

Smart Solutions

Dear Family,

For the next few weeks, we will be enjoying the theme *Smart Solutions*. We will read about characters who find clever and sometimes humorous solutions to everyday problems.

Theme-Related Activities to Do Together

Solve a Puzzle

Ask your child to help you select a puzzle. It could be a jigsaw or crossword puzzle or one from a children's magazine. Work on the puzzle together.

Take a Poll

Have your child ask neighbors and friends which languages they speak or read other than English, and list them. Challenge your child to discover as many different languages as possible.

Reading Comic Strips

Read a comic book or some comic strips with your child, paying attention to how the reader can tell which characters are talking and what they are thinking. Challenge your child to write a conversation between friends in comic-strip form.

Theme-Related Books to Enjoy Together!

Mr. Lincoln's Whiskers *by Karen Winnick. Boyds Mills 1996 (32p); also paper* A young girl writes to President Lincoln suggesting that he grow a beard to enhance his appearance and get more votes.

Too Many Tamales *by Gary Soto. Penguin 1993 (32p); also paper* When Maria fears she has lost her mother's wedding ring while making tamales, she and her cousins eat all twenty-four tamales in order to find it. Available in Spanish as *¡Qué montón de tamales!*

Doctor De Soto *by William Steig. Farrar 1982 (32p); also paper* Mouse-dentist Doctor De Soto and his wife must find a way to keep from being eaten by one of their large and hungry patients. Available in Spanish.

Meg Mackintosh and the Mystery at the Soccer Match *by Lucinda Landon. Secret Passage 1997 (48p)* In this solve-it-yourself mystery, the reader helps Meg find out what happened to the gold medal that disappeared from the awards table.

The Twins Strike Back *by Valerie Flournoy. Just Us 1994 (32p); also paper* Natalie and Nicole team up to show people that just because they are twins they don't have to think alike.

Not My Dog *by Colby Rodowsky. Farrar 1999 (69p)* Ellie has always wanted a puppy, but instead she gets Preston, her great-aunt's fully grown mutt.

Boletín

Soluciones sorprendentes

Estimada familia:

Durante las próximas semanas, vamos a tratar el tema *Soluciones sorprendentes*. Vamos a leer acerca de personajes que hallan soluciones ingeniosas y a veces cómicas a problemas cotidianos.

Actividades para hacer juntos

A resolver un acertijo

Juntos con su niño o niña, escojan un acertijo. Puede ser un rompecabezas o un crucigrama, o algo de una revista infantil. Trabajen juntos para resolver el acertijo.

Hacer una encuesta

Pida a su niño o niña que pregunte a sus vecinos y amigos qué idiomas hablan o leen además del inglés, y que haga una lista de las respuestas. Anime a su niño o niña a descubrir tantos idiomas como pueda.

Lectura de tiras cómicas

Lean juntos una revista de tiras cómicas o tiras cómicas de los periódicos, poniendo atención a cómo el lector sabe lo que cada personaje dice y piensa. Pida a su niño o niña que escriba una conversación entre amigos, con el formato de las tiras cómicas.

Libros relacionados al tema que pueden leer juntos

Mr. Lincoln's Whiskers *por Karen Winnick. Boyds Mills 1996 (32pp); también libro de bolsillo* Una niña le escribe al Presidente Lincoln, sugiriéndole que se deje crecer la barba para que se vea mejor y así pueda obtener más votos.

Too Many Tamales *por Gary Soto. Penguin 1993 (32pp); también libro de bolsillo* Cuando María teme haber perdido el anillo de bodas de su madre al preparar los tamales, ella y sus primos se comen los veinticuatro tamales en busca del anillo. Disponible en español con el título *¡Qué montón de tamales!*

Doctor De Soto *por William Steig. Farrar 1982 (32pp); también libro de bolsillo* El ratón dentista Doctor De Soto y su esposa deben encontrar cómo evitar ser comidos por uno de sus grandes y hambrientos pacientes. Disponible en español.

Meg Mackintosh and the Mystery at the Soccer Match *por Lucinda Landon. Secret Passage 1997 (48pp)* En este misterio, el lector debe ayudar a Meg a averiguar lo que sucedió con la medalla de oro que desapareció de la mesa de trofeos.

The Twins Strike Back *por Valerie Flournoy. Just Us 1994 (32pp); también libro de bolsillo* Natalie y Nicole se juntan para demostrarle a la gente que el solo hecho de ser gemelas no significa que piensan igual.

Not My Dog *por Colby Rodowsky. Farrar 1999 (69pp)* Ellie siempre ha querido tener un perrito pero, en su lugar, recibe a Preston, el perro ya grande de su tía abuela.

Selection Summaries

Cliff Hanger

Axel rock climbs in the mountains, where Axel's father, Dag, runs a rock climbing school. One day when a big storm comes near, Axel finds out his dog, Grits, is trapped on Cathedral Wall. Dag hears the news, so he and Axel set out to rescue Grits.

When they reach the bottom of Cathedral Wall, Dag counts the seconds between the lightning and the thunder and thinks they don't have enough time to rescue Grits before the storm arrives. But Axel sees Grits on a ledge. Axel is afraid that his dog will fall so he begins to climb.

After he climbs fifteen feet, Axel ropes himself to the cliff so he won't fall. He continues to climb and reaches the ledge where Grits is waiting.

The storm arrives. Axel and Grits wait out the storm on the ledge. Static electricity is all around them.

The storm moves on. Axel lowers Grits to his dad using a rope harness. But now he doesn't have enough rope left to climb all the way down. He climbs down about halfway. Then his dad points out a good route to take to get him to the ground. Axel finally reaches Dag and Grits, and they rest at the bottom of the cliff.

The Ballad of Mulan

A long time ago in China, there was a young woman named Mulan. She was upset because her father had been called to fight in a war. Mulan wanted to fight in her father's place.

Women were not allowed to be soldiers. So Mulan dressed like a man. She put on armor. She said a sad farewell to her family. Then she rode off with the troops.

It was hard work to be a soldier. Mulan missed her mother and her father. But it made Mulan happy to think that her father was safe.

Many soldiers died in the war. Mulan fought bravely. After ten years, the Emperor called Mulan to the palace. He wanted to reward Mulan's skill and leadership. Mulan asked the Emperor for a fast camel to take her home.

Mulan was happy to be back home. She changed out of her armor and into a dress. When the other soldiers came to see her, they were surprised. They had not known Mulan was a woman.

Today people still tell the story of Mulan's love for her family and her bravery in war.

The Lost and Found

One day at school, Wendell and Floyd were waiting outside the principal's office. They were in trouble because they had missed a math test. They said that a giant squid had trapped them in the bathroom. The boys thought they had no luck.

Mona Tudburn came to the office to look in the Lost and Found bin. She had lost her lucky hat. Mona fell in the bin and seemed to disappear! The boys decided to climb in after her.

Wendell and Floyd fell past lost toys and clothing. Mona was at the bottom. A sign pointed to the Hat Room. Floyd was worried that they would get lost.

In the Hat Room, the boys picked out lucky hats. Mona found her hat. It had been in her purse the whole time.

The children didn't know how to get back. They were lost in the Lost and Found! There were doors in all directions. Mona closed her eyes and pointed. The children went the way Mona picked.

After a long trip, the children got back to the office. Mona waited for her new friends while they talked to the principal. Then they all put on their lucky hats. The friends felt lucky together.

The Keeping Quilt

Long ago, Anna left Russia with her family. They came to America to live in New York City. But they missed their old home. Then Anna's mother had an idea. She would make a quilt! She cut shapes from an old dress, an uncle's shirt, and an aunt's apron. She cut Anna's shawl to make a border. Then she sewed the scraps together into a quilt. It helped her family remember the loved ones still in Russia.

When Anna grew up, Anna's mother gave her the quilt. Years later, Anna gave the quilt to Carle, her daughter. And in time, Carle passed the quilt on to her daughter Mary Ellen. Now the quilt belongs to Mary Ellen's daughter, the author of this story.

Over the years, the quilt became special. It welcomed new babies and kept old legs warm. Daughters were married under it. It was used as a tablecloth at birthdays and Sabbath meals. The quilt became an important part of many family gatherings.

The author calls the quilt the Keeping Quilt. It tells the family's special story. The author hopes to be as lucky as her mother. She hopes to tell the quilt's story to her grandchildren one day too.

Grandma's Records

Every year when school was over, I would stay with my grandma for the summer. My grandma was from Puerto Rico. We would spend lots of time listening to her favorite music together. One record was very special to her. When she played it, she would place her hand over her heart. The song reminded her of growing up in Puerto Rico. Sometimes Grandma would let me pick the records. Those were my favorite days.

Grandma's nephew, Sammy, played in the best band in Puerto Rico. One day Sammy and the band's lead singer came to visit. They gave us two tickets for the band's first New York concert.

We took the subway all the way up to the Bronx to the theater. The band put on a great show. The last song the band played was Grandma's special song. The singer dedicated it to her, and everyone in the theater placed their hands over their hearts.

As I grew up, I shared my own records with Grandma. She loved all of them. And now, when I play CDs in my studio, I'm reminded of the days when I listened to Grandma's special song.

The Talking Cloth

Amber's Aunt Phoebe is a collector of many interesting things. She tells wonderful stories about them when Amber visits her. Amber grows inside, just from learning what Aunt Phoebe knows.

Today Aunt Phoebe shows Amber a long, white piece of *adinkra* cloth from the country of Ghana. She says that once only kings or other royalty could wear it. She also tells Amber the meanings of the colors and symbols on the cloth. A white cloth means joy. Red means sadness, and blue means love. The symbols on the cloth stand for big ideas, like faith or love. Without saying a word, the long, silk cloth seems to talk!

Amber thinks about symbols she'd use for a cloth of her own. She also pictures the symbols she'd use on cloth for her baby brother or father.

Now Aunt Phoebe wraps the adinkra cloth around Amber. Amber pictures herself as a princess. Her family and everyone who has worn adinkra cloth stands around her. She feels herself growing inside, just from the knowing. And Amber smiles.

Dancing Rainbows

Every June, the Pueblo Indians of the San Juan Pueblo in New Mexico hold a big gathering. They call it Feast Day. It is a time of food and fun. It is also the time when Curt and his grandfather Andy will dance. So will the other members of Curt's tribe, the Tewas.

Each Tewa dance is special. It is also a prayer. The dancers pray for good crops. They dance to cure the sick and to show respect for the earth. They also dance to show they are thankful for rain, rainbows, and all living things.

On Feast Day Andy and Curt put on face paint and costumes. They rush to the plaza in the center of town. That is where the Tewas dance. Drums pound, bells jingle, and drummers sing. Young and old move to the drum beats. As soon as they can walk, Tewa children learn to dance. They dance proudly and with honor, just as the men and women do. At lunch people go home for a big feast. Then they dance again until the sun sets.

Andy has taught Curt and the other young Tewas the dances of their ancestors. Curt knows his grandfather is wise. He is proud to dance for rain and for rainbows.

Dogzilla

It was summer in the city of Mousopolis. The mice were gathered for a cookout. The food was on the grill and the mice were happy. The smells from the cookout filled the air. Then the ground began to shake. A strange sniffing sound was heard. A big monster came out of a nearby crater to join the cookout: Dogzilla!

The Big Cheese sent his army to stop the monster. They were very brave until Dogzilla breathed on them. Then they all ran away as fast as their little legs could carry them! The beast ate all of the food from their cookout. And then she started doing things that dogs like to do. She chased cars — right off the road! She chewed things — and the stores they were sold in! She had to be stopped.

The Big Cheese didn't know what to do. He went to an expert for help. The expert said that they had to scare Dogzilla out of town. So the mice decided to give Dogzilla something that all dogs fear: a bath! They hit the beast with lots of soap and warm water. Dogzilla quickly ran back to her crater in shock!

The mice were happy again. When they held their cookout the next summer, they were sure Dogzilla would not return. They were right about the beast, but there was one thing they had not thought of . . . puppies!

The Mysterious Giant of Barletta

In a small town in Italy called Barletta, there was a giant statue of a boy. He stood in the town square year in and year out. All the people lived their lives around him. Barletta was a peaceful town. The people thought it would always be that way.

But one day, the people heard that an army was coming to destroy their town! Everyone was scared. They did not have any way to protect themselves. The oldest woman in town, Zia Concetta, was very sad. She began talking to her old friend, the giant statue. She wished he would come to life to help protect the town of Barletta. And that is what he did!

Zia Concetta made a plan to save Barletta. While everyone in town hid, the giant went to sit outside of town with an onion. When the army arrived, they were stopped by the sight of a giant boy sitting in a puddle of tears. The captain of the army asked the giant why he was crying. The giant said he was sad because he was too small and weak to play with the other boys of his town. The army was scared. They began to wonder: If this huge boy was too small to play with the other boys, how big must the men in his town be? They did not stay to find out. They ran away from Barletta as fast as they could. And the giant returned to his spot in his peaceful, happy town.

Raising Dragons

When I was a little girl, I lived on a farm with my Ma and Pa. Pa raised our food and animals, and Ma took care of our home. I raised dragons.

I found my first dragon egg in Miller's cave. When it hatched, I named the dragon Hank and took him home with me. At first, my parents did not want to see or hear about Hank. But I took good care of him. When he was bigger, he took me flying over the countryside at night. It was grand!

Hank helped out around the farm. He plowed the fields. He kept bugs away from the crops. He kept Ma's tomato plants cool during a heat wave. Ma made treats for Hank to eat, and he kept getting bigger.

That year, Hank and I planted too much corn. Pa did not know what to do. But Hank had an idea. He used his fire-breath to turn the corn into popcorn! We sold all of it and made a bunch of money, but it got people talking. They started making a fuss out of our having a dragon on our farm. I realized Hank would have to go.

I read about a dragon island in the middle of the ocean, so I took Hank there. When it was time to return to the farm, I was very sad. Just as I was about to leave, Hank gave me a present: a bunch of dragon eggs! Boy, oh, boy, when those eggs began hatching, I had my work cut out for me!

The Garden of Abdul Gasazi

One day, Miss Hester left her dog Fritz with Alan Mitz to watch. All morning Alan tried to keep Fritz from chewing the furniture. Then it was time for Fritz's afternoon walk.

Fritz led Alan to a door to a garden. A sign near the door read, "No Dogs in This Garden. Abdul Gasazi, Magician." As Alan turned away, Fritz pulled hard, broke his leash, and ran into the garden.

Alan chased after Fritz, but he could not catch him. Soon, Alan found a big house. At the big house, Alan met a big man: Mr. Gasazi. Alan told Mr. Gasazi that he was sorry that Fritz ran into his garden. Could he please have Fritz back? Mr. Gasazi said that he could have Fritz, but that Fritz was no longer a dog. Mr. Gasazi had turned Fritz into a duck!

Sadly, Alan picked up the duck and headed home. But before he could get very far, the wind blew off his hat. The duck slipped out of his arms, caught the hat in its mouth, and flew up into the sky!

As Alan walked slowly home, he thought Fritz was gone for sure. But when he got to Miss Hester's house, Fritz was there and he was a dog again! Miss Hester told Alan that Mr. Gasazi must have been teasing him. But after Alan left, Miss Hester found Fritz chewing on Alan's hat.

Nights of the Pufflings

Halla [HATT-lah] lives on an island in Iceland. One day she stands on a high cliff by the sea. She sees a bird with an orange beak. It is a puffin! Soon there are many puffins in the sky. The puffins come ashore to the island once a year. They lay eggs in burrows in the cliffs. Then they raise baby pufflings.

The pufflings hide in the safe burrows. Their parents bring them fish. The pufflings grow bigger. They leave the burrows for the first time. They try to launch themselves off the cliffs and into the sea.

But the pufflings have a problem. They are not good at flying yet. Many land in Halla's village, not the sea. Then they are lost. They cannot find the sea. There are cats, dogs, and cars in the village. It is not a safe place for the little pufflings. So the children of the island help them!

Halla and her friends look for lost pufflings in the village. They catch them and put them in boxes. Then they take the boxes to the sea and set the pufflings free. Now they are safe! Halla tells the pufflings good-bye and good luck.

Seal Surfer

One spring day, Ben and his granddad visited the beach. They saw a seal on the rocks. At first they thought the seal was hurt. Then they saw that she had a new baby seal with her.

Ben and his granddad watched the seals all spring. They fed them fish. In autumn, they saw the baby learn to swim. The seals even seemed to like music that Ben's granddad played.

In winter, there were bad storms. When spring came, they did not see the baby seal. They thought the seal died in the storms.

In summer, Ben went surfing. One day, something fast and dark swooped under his surfboard. It was the baby seal! Ben and the seal surfed the waves together.

The next day, a big wave made Ben fall off his board. His head hit a rock. Sand and water filled his nose and mouth. He fell deeper. Everything was dark. Then the seal pushed him up out of the water! The seal flipped Ben onto his board. Ben was safe. For the rest of the summer, he surfed with the seal.

Next summer, the seal came back with a baby of her own. Then Ben knew he would surf with the seals every summer. Maybe someday Ben would bring his grandchildren to meet the seals too.

Two Days in May

My name is Sonia and I live in a big city. One May morning, I looked out my window. I saw five deer grazing in my garden. They had walked far looking for food. Then they had wandered into my city. Everyone in my neighborhood came to see them.

Then we had bad news. The deer would starve in the city. The woods where the deer lived had been cut down to build roads and towns. There was no place for the deer to go. So the city's animal control office was going to shoot the deer.

The people in my neighborhood all said that we would not let the deer be shot! We called a wildlife rescue worker who finds new homes for animals in danger. Then we stayed by the deer all day and night to keep them safe until help came.

The next morning, the wildlife rescue worker came. He took the deer to some woods away from the city. There the deer would be safe and have lots to eat. We were all happy that we had worked together to help the deer. Everyone in my neighborhood became better friends. I still like to think of the deer in their new home.

Across the Wide Dark Sea

My family waved good-bye to our friends and home. I looked out at the wide dark sea. It never seemed to end. We were going to cross that huge sea in a ship to get to a strange new land.

Our journey was hard. The cramped little ship was full of people and things. It was cold and wet. There were storms. Waves crashed and the wind blew. Our ship cracked and leaked. Many people were seasick.

Months later, we saw land. We were happy. But what would the land be like? Were there people there? We did not know.

We built a settlement town. Soon a bad winter came. Many people were sick and hungry. Half of them did not survive.

In spring, Indians came to our settlement. They taught us how to catch fish and grow crops. We would have food to eat next winter.

In April, we watched our ship sail back to our old home. Now we were alone in the new land. I felt scared and sad. Then I looked at our town and crops. I felt proud. I saw how much we had done. I knew we had much more work to do. So I turned around and walked back to my new home.

Yunmi and Halmoni's Trip

Yunmi was on her first airplane ride with her grandmother, Halmoni. They were going to visit family in Korea. Halmoni used to live there. Now she lived in New York City with Yunmi and her parents. But Halmoni's pets, friends, and other grandchildren were still in Korea. Halmoni had not seen them for a long time. Yunmi had never met them.

Everyone in Korea was glad to see them. Yunmi's cousins took her sightseeing all over the city of Seoul. They had a big picnic.

Yunmi saw that Halmoni was happy in Korea. She heard her cousins tell Halmoni that they did not want her to leave. Yunmi started to worry. What if Halmoni wanted to stay in Korea? What if she did not want to live with Yunmi anymore?

Halmoni said that her home was in New York with Yunmi. She told Yunmi to remember that Halmoni's family in Korea was Yunmi's family too. They were lucky because they both had two families! Yunmi knew Halmoni was right. So Yunmi decided she would ask her cousins to visit them in New York.

Trapped by the Ice!

The *Endurance* was trapped in the ice! Sir Ernest Shackleton and his crew wanted to be the first people to cross the South Pole in Antarctica. But their ship, the *Endurance*, was being crushed by the ice. Soon it broke apart and sank.

The men camped on floating sheets of ice. They waited for the ice floes to carry them closer to land. One man was attacked by a real-life sea monster called a sea leopard. Another fell into a huge crevasse in the ice.

The men sailed in lifeboats to a deserted place called Elephant Island. Shackleton told them to camp on the island until he came back. Then he and five men left in a lifeboat to find help.

Giant waves and a storm almost sank their lifeboat. They landed on South Georgia Island. They hiked across rocky terrain and climbed icy mountains. Finally, they found people to help them.

Shackleton got a bigger boat. He went back to get the men on Elephant Island. It took him three months to break through the ice. But he did it! Everyone survived. At last they were going home. Shackleton was a hero!

Pepita Talks Twice

Pepita spoke Spanish and English. Today, Pepita wanted to get home before her brother. She wanted to teach their dog, Lobo, to fetch. On the way home, Pepita stopped to tell Mr. Hobbs what a lady who spoke only Spanish wanted from his store. Pepita stopped to speak Spanish and English for her friend's mother and her Aunt Rosa too.

When Pepita got home, she was too late. Her brother was teaching Lobo to fetch. If she hadn't stopped to speak Spanish and English, she would have been home first. Pepita decided not to speak Spanish anymore. She was tired of talking twice!

But there were a lot of problems with speaking only English. Pepita could not ask for tacos with salsa. Those were Spanish words. Lobo would not listen to her when she spoke English and called him "Wolf." At school, Pepita could not help the new student who spoke only Spanish. Pepita could not sing Spanish songs with her friends.

The next morning, Lobo chased a ball into the road. A car was coming! Lobo did not come when Pepita called him Wolf. Pepita screamed *Lobo!*, his Spanish name. Lobo turned back just in time. He was safe. Pepita was happy. Now she knew it was good to speak two languages.

Poppa's New Pants

My name is George. Poppa and I helped Grandma Tiny clean the house for Big Mama and Aunt Viney's visit. Then Poppa and I went to the store. Poppa bought a pair of gray pants with a red plaid pattern. The pants were too long.

When we got home, Big Mama and Aunt Viney were there. The women were all too tired to hem Poppa's pants. Poppa draped the pants over the rocking chair.

That night, I slept in the kitchen because Big Mama and Aunt Viney were in my room. As I fell asleep, a small, white shape came in. Later a tall, thin white shape came through the doorway. Finally, a big, white shape came into the room! Each time, I was scared and hid under the covers. I heard the rocking chair creak, a snipping sound, and a rustling. I kept telling myself that ghosts were not real.

In the morning, there was a surprise. Grandma Tiny said she had cut six inches off of Poppa's pants during the night. Then Aunt Viney and Big Mama said they had each hemmed the pants too. So they were the ghosts I had seen! Poppa held up the pants and started laughing. They only reached to his knees! But I didn't mind. Now the pants fit me.

Ramona Quimby, Age 8

It was a dismal, rainy Sunday. Ramona sat watching the rain pelting against the window. She hated dreary days like this. The whole Quimby family was grouchy and discouraged. Mrs. Quimby was upset that Ramona hadn't cleaned her room. Beezus was angry because she wasn't allowed to sleep over at Mary Jane's. Ramona's father was trying to study.

Mr. Quimby was tired of the family's grumping around. He said that the family was going out to dinner. They were going to enjoy it too. That was an order!

The food at the Whopperburger tasted wonderful. A change was just what the family needed. Everyone felt happy and companionable.

An old man at the restaurant missed his own family. He thought the Quimbys were a nice family. So he paid for their dinner! The Quimbys were surprised. They had not acted like a nice family that day. Then Mrs. Quimby said that they were a nice family. It was just that nobody is nice all the time.

It was a happy ending to the day. But Ramona knew that tomorrow the Quimbys would start all over again.

Assignment Cards

Reading Routines

Before You Read . . .

- Read the title and look at the illustrations. Ask yourself, "Can I guess what this story will be about?"

As You Read . . .

- Pause to think about how the characters act and feel. Then predict what you think will happen.

- Complete your Cause and Effect Chart on **Practice Book** page 12 with causes and effects from the story.

- Think of questions to ask your classmates after you read.

Theme 1: Off to Adventure!

Live the Adventure

Setting

Reread page 21. Then picture yourself in the mountains with Axel. What do you hear, smell, and taste? What do you see and feel?

Write a paragraph that gives more details about the story setting. Use story clues and your own ideas to tell more about the mountains and the storm. Make your readers feel as if they are there too. Share your work with others in your group.

Theme 1: Off to Adventure!

Literature Discussion

With a small group of classmates, talk over your questions and ideas about the story. Also discuss these questions:

- How does Axel feel during his adventure? How can you tell?

- What is Dag thinking and feeling when Axel is up on the cliff?

- What's the most exciting adventure you've ever had? Share your story.

Theme 1: Off to Adventure!

Bent Like a Hairpin

Similes

As Axel climbs onto Monkey Ledge, the author describes him as being *bent like a hairpin*.

This is a **simile**. It uses *like* or *as* to describe how two different things seem alike. Axel's bent-in-half position might remind someone of the shape of a metal hairpin.

With a partner, find two other similes in the story. List each one, and tell how the two different things seem alike. Then try to make up a simile of your own to describe the frightened dog stranded on the ledge.

Theme 1: Off to Adventure!

Reading Routines

Before You Read . . .

- Go through the story. Be sure to read the title and look at the illustrations. Then think about what might happen in the story.

As You Read . . .

- Pause to monitor what you are reading. If you don't understand something, reread a few pages to clarify it.

- Complete your Inferences Chart on **Practice Book** page 32. Write story clues, what you know, and an inference that answers each question.

- Think of questions to ask after you finish reading.

Theme 1: Off to Adventure!

What to Choose

Style

The author of *The Ballad of Mulan*, Song Nan Zhang, chose to tell the story in a certain way. The words and ideas he picked make up his writing **style**. Use these questions to talk about the author's writing style:

- What words gave you a certain feeling or made pictures in your mind? Why do you think the author gave some details — such as Mulan's worries — but left out others?

- A ballad is a poem or song that tells a story in a simple way. How has the author made this Chinese legend seem like a ballad?

Theme 1: Off to Adventure!

Like a Person

Figurative Language

On page 65, the author says that Mulan heard *the sound of the river crying*. He makes the river seem like a person because it "cries." This special use of language is called **personification**.

With a partner, choose four objects from the story and illustrations, such as Mulan's loom, a cold mountain wind, the flags of the enemy soldiers, or the village gate. Write a sentence that describes each object as if it were moving, acting, or thinking like a person would.

Theme 1: Off to Adventure!

Literature Discussion

In a small group, discuss your questions and ideas about the story. Also talk about these questions:

- Mulan does something unusual for women of her time. How is she like a real person or story character you know?

- Do you know other characters who disguise themselves? Why do they do this — to carry out a task, reach a goal, or make a dream come true? Describe what happens.

- A hero is a person who is remembered for wise actions and brave deeds. Would you call Mulan a hero? Why or why not?

Theme 1: Off to Adventure!

Why She Acts That Way

Motivation

To understand a character like Mulan, you must think about why she acts, speaks, and feels as she does. What causes her actions is called her **motivation.**

With a partner, figure out the motivation of Mulan and other characters in one of the scenes given below. Jot down your ideas, and then share them with the group.

Pages 56–61   Mulan and her mother

Pages 72–75   the Emperor and Mulan

Pages 78–82   Mulan at home

Theme 1: Off to Adventure!

Reading Routines

Before You Read . . .

- Quickly go through the story. Read the title and look at the illustrations. Ask yourself, "What is this story about?"

As You Read . . .

- Pause to summarize the important parts of the story. Remember that when you summarize, you retell the big ideas in your own words.

- Complete your Event Map on **Practice Book** page 48.

- Think of questions you can ask after you read.

Theme 1: Off to Adventure!

Assignment Card 1   The Lost and Found

Full of Surprises

Suspense

Are you surprised when Mona disappears inside the Lost and Found bin? The boys sure are! How can she get lost there? Where has she gone? The author wants you to wonder what will happen, so he builds **suspense** into his story. He hopes that you'll ask questions about what happens next. Then you'll want to read on to find the answers.

Get together with a partner. List three other spots in the story where the author builds suspense. For each spot, write two questions you have about what will happen in the Lost and Found bin.

Theme 1: Off to Adventure!

Literature Discussion

With a small group of classmates, talk over your questions and ideas about the story. Also discuss these questions:

- Why does the Lost and Found seem so strange?

- Why don't Wendell and Mona pay attention to Floyd when he warns them about getting lost in the Lost and Found? Do you think they are being wise? Explain.

- Would you like to have Wendell and Floyd as friends in real life? Why or why not?

Theme 1: Off to Adventure!

Telling Tales

Humorous Dialogue

On page 102, Floyd wonders if the principal knows about the lake inside the Lost and Found bin. That may seem funny. So are some other things the children say. Their **dialogue** adds humor to the strange adventure. In a small group, talk about their dialogue.

- Reread pages 97, 101, and 105. How do Wendell's ideas about getting lost change? How might this seem funny to readers?

- Reread pages 108–109 to yourselves. What is funny about the dialogue? Take turns being Wendell, Mona, and Floyd. Read the dialogue aloud as if you feel as those characters do.

Theme 1: Off to Adventure!

Reading Routines

Before You Read . . .

- Read the title and look at the illustrations. What do you think will happen in the story?

As You Read . . .

- Stop to evaluate how well the author and illustrator tells the story of her family's Keeping Quilt.

- Fill in your Author's Family Chart on **Practice Book** page 96.

- Think of questions you can discuss with your classmates after you have finished reading.

Theme 2: Celebrating Traditions

Be a Detective

Making Inferences

As you read *The Keeping Quilt*, be a detective. Use the illustrations, story clues, and what you know from real life to answer these questions:

- What can you infer about Anna's new life from the story details on pages 162–163?

- How do you think Anna felt when she moved to America from Russia?

- Look at the illustrations on pages 162–163. When do you think this part of the story takes place?

Theme 2: Celebrating Traditions

Characters Have Feelings Too!

Character's Feelings

Why do you think Anna's mother decides to make a quilt? How might she have come up with the idea? What makes the idea a good one? Use what you know from the story and from your own experience to make inferences that answer these questions. Then write a short scene between Anna's mother and a neighbor. Have them discuss why they want to make the quilt. Act out your scene with a partner.

Theme 2: Celebrating Traditions

Literature Discussion

Form a small group with several classmates. Discuss your answers to these questions and to any other questions you may have thought of while reading.

- How does the quilt become more and more important to Anna's family?

- What traditions does Anna's mother bring from backhome Russia? What new ones does she start?

- If you made your own Keeping Quilt, what would it look like?

Theme 2: Celebrating Traditions

Tell the Quilt's History

Time Line

If the Keeping Quilt were included in a museum exhibit about family traditions, a time line would help visitors understand the quilt's history. Create a time line that shows the order of the different owners of the quilt.

At the right end of the line, write the year 2000. Count backwards from the year 2000, marking off the line and labeling it every ten years. Suppose that Patricia, Mary Ellen, Carle, and Anna each owned the quilt for twenty-five years, and that Anna's mother owned it for ten years. Next to the dates on the time line, write short sentences telling how each owner used the quilt.

Theme 2: Celebrating Traditions

Reading Routines

Before You Read . . .

- Quickly look through the selection. Read the title and look at the photographs. Think about what you might learn.

As You Read . . .

- Pause to think about what you've read. Make up questions that test a reader's knowledge of the selection.

- Work on the Categories Chart on **Practice Book** page 114 by writing details about Anthony's life in the correct boxes.

- Come up with questions you can ask your classmates after you have finished reading.

Theme 2: Celebrating Traditions

Assignment Card 5 | Grandma's Records

Literature Discussion

With a small group of classmates, talk over your questions and ideas about the story. Also discuss these questions:

- How do you think the concert makes the boy feel?

- How can you tell that Grandma loves her music?

- If you could take Grandma to a concert, what kind of music would it be? Why?

Theme 2: Celebrating Traditions

a Reporter!

from the boy's point of view. This helps the
now the boy thinks and feels. For example, on
s that Cortijo's band made "familiar songs sound
fre... concert. If you were a newspaper reporter writing a
review ...e performance, you might want to interview other people
who were there to get their point of view.

Pick someone else who was at the concert: Grandma, another
audience member, or one of the musicians. Write some questions you
might ask this person. Then write the answers from their point of
view.

Theme 2: Celebrating Traditions

Reading Routines

Before You Read . . .

- Preview the story by reading the title and looking at the illustrations to learn what the story is about.

As You Read . . .

- Stop and use your own words to summarize important story events and main ideas.

- Complete your Cluster Map on **Practice Book** page 131.

- Think of questions about the story to discuss with your classmates when you have finished reading.

Theme 2: Celebrating Traditions

Words, Words, Words!

Repetition

Reread the first two sentences of the story and the last sentence on page 220. Which word is repeated? Why do you think the author did this? How does it help you understand Aunt Phoebe, her house, and how Amber feels about her?

Work with a partner to rewrite these three sentences in a different way. How do the rewritten sentences change the sound and meaning of the story? Next, choose a part of the story and rewrite each sentence so that words or phrases are repeated. Compare your sentences with the author's. How have the sound and meaning changed?

Theme 2: Celebrating Traditions

Literature Discussion

With several of your classmates, gather into a small group. Discuss your answers to the following questions and to any others you came up with.

- Why is Amber interested in her aunt's stories and objects?

- Do you have a family member who you like to visit as much as Amber likes to visit Aunt Phoebe? Why?

- Why do you think Aunt Phoebe brings back items from her travels?

- In what way does your own clothing "talk" or tell how you feel?

Theme 2: Celebrating Traditions

Secret Code

Symbols

Symbols are pictures, shapes, or designs that stand for something else. For example, a common symbol is a stop sign. Even if the word STOP were not written on the sign, we would still recognize its eight-sided shape and red color. We would know that the sign is a symbol meaning, "Stop!"

Think of other symbols. Many symbols have something in common with what they stand for. For example, on page 226, Amber decides that a grubby handprint is a good symbol for her messy little brother. Use story clues to think of colors and symbols for cloths that Amber and Aunt Phoebe might wear.

Theme 2: Celebrating Traditions

Reading Routines

Before You Read . . .

- Take some time to look through the selection and think about what you might learn.

As You Read . . .

- Monitor your reading by asking yourself if you understand and by rereading or reading ahead to clarify.

- Complete the Cluster Diagram on **Practice Book** page 146.

- Think of a few questions or ideas about the selection to discuss with your classmates after you have finished reading.

Theme 2: Celebrating Traditions

Literature Discussion

Form a small group with several other classmates. Discuss the following questions and any other questions or ideas you thought of while reading.

- What do the facts about the Feast Day celebration show about the Garcia family and the Tewa community?

- What would you like most about visiting San Juan Pueblo and the Feast Day celebration?

- Does your community, neighborhood, school, or family celebrate any special days together? How does everyone help?

Theme 2: Celebrating Traditions

Make Some Noise

Onomatopoeia

Onomatopoeia is the name for words that imitate sounds. For example, on pages 247 and 249, we learn that the Feast Day drums *BOOM!* and Curt's bells *jingle*. Other examples of onomatopoeia are *buzz*, *meow*, *beep*, *honk*, *chirp*, *moo*, and *vroom!*

Pick a scene from the selection, such as the Garcia house on the day before Feast Day. Make a list of onomatopoeic words for all the sounds you would hear if you visited that scene. For example, the dogs might *woof*, the fire might *crackle*, and the cooking food might *sizzle*. If you can't think of a word for a certain sound, make one up!

Theme 2: Celebrating Traditions

Reading Routines

Before You Read . . .

- Read the title and cast of characters. Quickly look at the illustrations. Ask yourself, "What will happen?"

As You Read . . .

- Pause to evaluate how you feel about what you are reading. Does the story seem extremely goofy?

- Complete your Fantasy and Realism Chart on **Practice Book** page 196. List make-believe and realistic story details.

- Think of questions to ask your classmates after you read.

Theme 3: Incredible Stories

Puppy Point of View

Character's Perspective

This story is told from the point of view of the mice. The reader experiences the same sights, sounds, and smells as the mice do. But how might this story be different if it were told from Dogzilla's point of view?

Think about how Dogzilla might feel about the mice, and why she might act like she does. What sights, sounds, and smells would Dogzilla experience? Work with a partner to write about Dogzilla's first meeting with the mice from Dogzilla's perspective.

Theme 3: Incredible Stories

Literature Discussion

Form a small group with several of your classmates. Discuss your answers to the following questions and any other questions or ideas you may have thought of while reading the story.

- Do you think Dogzilla is a terrifying and monstrous creature? Explain.

- How does the story use fantasy and realism together? Find examples of each in the story.

- Do you agree with the author that this story is "extremely goofy"? Explain.

Theme 3: Incredible Stories

Man or Mouse?

Anthropomorphism

When a writer creates animal characters that think, look, or act like people, this is called **anthropomorphism**. That's a pretty big word, isn't it?

Read the text and look at the illustration on pages 322–323. What examples of **anthropomorphism** can you find? What other examples can you find of this technique in the story? In a small group, write down your ideas. Then list ways that animals and humans act the same in real life.

Theme 3: Incredible Stories

Reading Routines

Before You Read . . .

- Quickly go through the story. Read the title and look at the illustrations. Ask yourself, "What is this story about? What's going to happen?"

As You Read . . .

- Pause to think about the important ideas. Make up questions that might test a reader's knowledge of the story.

- Complete the Action Plan on **Practice Book** page 216. Fill in details about the steps the story characters follow to solve their problem.

Theme 3: Incredible Stories

See the Sights!

Be a Tour Guide

Think of yourself as a tour guide to the town of Barletta. Write a dialogue between yourself and a group of tourists. Think about what kinds of questions the tourists might ask about the mysterious statue. Where did the statue come from? When did it arrive? Who is the statue modeled after? Include the questions and your answers in the dialogue. Look at pages 336–337 for ideas.

Theme 3: Incredible Stories

Literature Discussion

Form a small group. Discuss your answers to these and other questions you may have thought of while reading.

- Why might Zia Concetta want to stay in Barletta? What makes you think so?

- What do you think Zia Concetta and the Mysterious Giant are going to do to solve the problem?

- How is this tale like other folktales you know? How is it different?

- In what ways are the Giant and Dogzilla the same? How are they different?

Theme 3: Incredible Stories

Character Chat

Folktale Characters

Folktales are fun to read, but they also teach little lessons about being kind, brave, or patient. Think about the main characters in *The Mysterious Giant of Barletta*. What traits do the characters have that help them to overcome the story problem?

- Think about Zia Concetta's age, wisdom, and cleverness.

- Think about the Giant's loyalty, size, gentleness, and bravery.

In a small group, discuss your ideas. Then work together to create a list of additional traits that help characters in other folktales solve a problem or achieve a goal.

Theme 3: Incredible Stories

Reading Routines

Before You Read . . .

- Go through the story. Read the title and look at the illustrations. Ask yourself, "What is this story about?"

As You Read . . .

- Pause to think about how the characters act and feel. Use story clues and what you know to predict what will happen.

- Complete your Conclusions Chart on **Practice Book** page 231. Write story details and conclusions.

- Come up with questions to ask after you read.

Theme 3: Incredible Stories

Assignment Card 7   Raising Dragons

There's No Place Like Home

Setting

Think about Hank's size, fiery breath, and eating habits. What kind of a house might he live in? What sorts of things would a dragon need in his home? Draw a diagram of what the inside of Hank's house might look like. Label each part and explain how it is used or why you included it. Be as creative as you want!

Theme 3: Incredible Stories

Literature Discussion

With several of your classmates, gather into a small group. Discuss your answers to the following questions and to any others you have.

- How does Hank feel about the girl in the story? How can you tell?

- Do you think the girl will be able to keep her dragon? Why or why not?

- If you found a baby dragon, what would you do with it? Why?

- How do you think most parents would react if their child became friends with a dragon?

Theme 3: Incredible Stories

A Dragon Dinner

Create a Menu

Work together in a small group to design and create a menu for a restaurant on the dragon island. Include appetizers, main courses, desserts, and drinks that a dragon might enjoy. Look at menus from real restaurants and on page 376 of the story for ideas.

You may want to include a brief history of your restaurant and its owner on the back of the menu.

Theme 3: Incredible Stories

Reading Routines

Before You Read . . .

- Go through the story. Be sure to read the title and look at the illustrations. Think about what might happen in the story.

As You Read . . .

- Pause to monitor your reading. If you don't understand something in the story, reread the page to clarify it. Or, read ahead — that might help too.

- Complete your Story Map on **Practice Book** page 246 with details about the characters, setting, and plot.

- Think of questions to ask others after you read.

Theme 3: Incredible Stories

You Decide!

Decision Making

Do you think Alan should continue to look for Fritz? Here's one way to decide. Divide a piece of paper into two columns.

- In the first column, write all the reasons you think Alan should look for the lost dog.

- In the second column, write all the reasons you think Alan should stop looking for Fritz.

Then decide what you think Alan should do. Write your decision and an explanation of it at the bottom of your paper.

Theme 3: Incredible Stories

Literature Discussion

In a small group, discuss these questions and any others you may have thought of while reading *The Garden of Abdul Gasazi*.

- Would you like Fritz for a pet? Why or why not?

- Even though he is bruised and tired, Alan continues to look for Fritz. What words would you use to describe Alan?

- How does the author build excitement and suspense? What words and picture details add to this mood?

- What kind of person is Abdul Gasazi? Give details from the story to support your answer.

Theme 3: Incredible Stories

Reading Routines

Before You Read . . .

- Read the title and look at the photographs. Ask yourself, "What might I learn in this selection?"

As You Read . . .

- Pause to evaluate how you feel about what you read. Does the author make the event seem important and exciting?

- Complete the Puffin Fact Chart on **Practice Book** page 4. List facts about the pufflings in the boxes.

- Think of questions to ask your classmates after you read.

Theme 4: Animal Habitats

Literature Discussion

Nights of the Pufflings is a nonfiction book. This means that everything in the story really happened almost exactly how the author describes it. Nonfiction can be hard to write. In groups, discuss the following questions.

- The author uses photos to help tell the story. Would reading the book be different without the photos?

- If you could interview Halla, what would you ask her?

- Do you think it is important to study puffins and other birds? Give reasons for your answer.

Theme 4: Animal Habitats

What's in a Picture?

Evaluating Photographs

Look through the book and think about what the photos tell you about the facts and feelings in this story.

- In pairs, choose photos that you think give you a lot of information and help explain the story. Explain to your partner why you think these photos are important.

- Then, think of photos that you wish were included. Explain your reasons.

- Share your results with the rest of your group.

Theme 4: Animal Habitats

Assignment Cards

Reading Routines

Before You Read . . .

- Go through the story. Be sure to read the title and look at the illustrations. Ask yourself, "What's going to happen?"

As You Read . . .

- Pause to summarize parts of the story.

- Complete the Venn Diagram on **Practice Book** page 23. Write ways that Ben and the seal are different and alike.

- Think of questions to discuss.

Theme 4: Animal Habitats

Who's Telling the Story?

Character's Perspective

This story is told in the "third person," which means that it is told without using the pronoun *I*, *me*, *we*, and *us*. Most of the story is told in the third person from Ben's perspective. In pairs, answer the following questions.

- At some points, the story shifts to the young seal's perspective. Why do you think the author changes perspective in these places?

- How do you think the story would be different if it were told from the perspective of the young seal only?

Theme 4: Animal Habitats

Literature Discussion

In small groups, discuss the following questions.

- What is the young seal's natural habitat?

- What are some of the challenges and risks of the young seal's habitat? How does she learn to overcome these challenges?

- Why do you think Ben and his grandfather like to watch the seals?

- Why do you think people are interested in watching animals in their natural habitats?

Theme 4: Animal Habitats

Where Are the Characters?

Setting

The setting is the place and time in which a story takes place. In pairs, do the following activities.

- Discuss these questions: What is the setting in *Seal Surfer*? How does the setting change? How do changes in the setting affect the story?

- Choose a different setting for the story. Write a brief description of this new setting. Also, write about how the characters and plot would change if the story took place in this new setting.

Theme 4: Animal Habitats

Reading Routines

Before You Read . . .

- Read the title and look at the illustrations. Think about what might happen as the story unfolds.

As You Read . . .

- Pause to monitor what you are reading. If you don't understand something in the story, reread to clarify it.

- Complete the Decisions Chart on **Practice Book** page 39. Write your opinions about the characters' actions.

- Think of questions to ask your classmates.

Theme 4: Animal Habitats

What's the Point?

Author's Viewpoint

An author may tell a story for many different reasons: to inform the reader of something, to convince the reader of something, or just to entertain.

In pairs, discuss why you think Harriet Peck Taylor wrote *Two Days in May*. Write a list of the reasons you come up with, and then discuss which reason seems most likely. Share your results with the group.

Theme 4: Animal Habitats

Literature Discussion

In small groups, discuss the following questions.

- What would you do if you were Sonia?

- The deer help to bring Sonia's neighbors together. What other things could bring her neighborhood together?

- Do you think Sonia's neighbors did the right thing by calling the animal rescue organization? Why or why not?

Theme 4: Animal Habitats

When *I* Tell the Story . . .

Point of View

This story is told in what is called the "first person," which means that it is told using the pronouns *I, me, we,* and *us.*

- From whose point of view is the story told? Why do you think the author chose to tell the story from this point of view?

A story can also be told in the "third person." This means that the story is told without using the pronouns *I, me, we,* and *us.*

- How do you think the story would be different if it were told in the third person? Rewrite page 90 in the third person. How is the feeling of the story different?

Theme 4: Animal Habitats

Reading Routines

Before You Read . . .

- Go through the story. Read the title and look at the illustrations. Ask yourself, "What's going to happen?"

As You Read . . .

- Pause to think about the important ideas you've read. Make up questions to test a reader's understanding of the story.

- Complete the Inferences Chart on **Practice Book** page 86. Write story clues, what you know, and an inference to answer each question.

Theme 5: Voyagers

Decisions, Decisions

Problem Solving

What did the Pilgrims bring on the *Mayflower* to start their lives in the new land? Find out from the list on page 159 and from other parts of the story.

What else do you think the Pilgrims might have needed? Discuss this with a partner. To help you decide, use story details and information you know about living as the Pilgrims did. Then make a more complete list of things the Pilgrims might have needed. Star the items you think are the most important things for the Pilgrims' survival. Share your ideas with the group.

Theme 5: Voyagers

Literature Discussion

With a small group, talk over your questions and ideas about the story. Also discuss these questions:

- How do you think the sailors might have felt about taking the Pilgrims to settle in a new land?

- The cracked beam was one problem the Pilgrims had to solve. What other problems do you think they might have faced on the voyage?

- Why do you think the Pilgrims were willing to risk their lives and families in order to start a new life?

Theme 5: Voyagers

Making a Hard Choice

Making Judgments

Picture yourself living in England in 1620. You are offered a chance to sail on the *Mayflower* with the Pilgrims. Is it wise for you to go with them to start a new life in an unknown land?

As a group, discuss the question. Make a list of the good and bad points of going to the new land or of staying behind in England.

Write a paragraph that gives your opinion. Tell whether you think it is wise to go with the Pilgrims. Explain why you think as you do.

Theme 5: Voyagers

Reading Routines

Before You Read . . .

- Go through the story. Read the title and look at the illustrations. Ask yourself, "What might happen in this story?"

As You Read . . .

- Pause to think about the characters' feelings and actions. Then predict what you think will happen next.

- Complete your Character Chart on **Practice Book** page 106. Fill in information about Yunmi.

- Think of questions to ask after you read.

Theme 5: Voyagers

One and the Same

Synonyms

To make their writing interesting, authors might use **synonyms**, or words with the same or nearly the same meanings. Here are some synonym pairs:

> scared   frightened
>
> happy   merry

With a partner, find four pairs of synonyms on pages 194–195. Then list four other words from the story, and write a synonym for each one. Get together with the group and share your work.

Theme 5: Voyagers

Literature Discussion

With a small group, talk over your questions and ideas about the story. Also discuss these questions:

- How do you think Yunmi feels about her visit to Korea? How can you tell?

- How has Yunmi and Halmoni's relationship changed?

- Compare and contrast Yunmi's trip to a trip you've taken. How were your experiences like Yunmi's? How were they different?

Theme 5: Voyagers

Following Directions

Quiet Games

Cat's cradle is a game that began in Asia. Two people take turns looping string over each other's fingers to make different figures. The art of paper folding, known as origami in Japan, is practiced in Korea and in other Asian countries. Shapes of animals, flowers, and other objects are created by folding paper instead of cutting it.

Learn how to play cat's cradle or fold an origami shape. Then teach it to others in the group.

Theme 5: Voyagers

Reading Routines

Before You Read . . .

- Read the title and the first journal entry. Look at the illustrations. What might you learn in this selection?

As You Read . . .

- Pause to monitor your reading. If you don't understand something, reread the page to clarify it.

- Complete your Text Organization Chart on **Practice Book** page 121. Fill in information about each text feature.

- Think of questions to ask after you read.

Theme 5: Voyagers

You Were There

Point of View

How would this story be different if a crew member described the dangerous trip? One way is that he'd tell it from the **first-person** point of view, using the words *I*, *me*, *we*, and *us*. In a small group, discuss how else the story would change. To help, use these questions:

- What details might the crew member feel are important to tell? What details might he leave out?

- How would the crew member's story be affected by his feelings and experiences? How might hearing him tell the story help you understand the dangers the crew faced?

Theme 5: Voyagers

Literature Discussion

In a small group, talk over your questions and ideas about the selection. Also discuss these questions:

- What challenges do Shackleton and his men face before and after the *Endurance* is trapped by the ice?

- How do you think Shackleton feels after the *Endurance* is trapped? How do you think the crew feels? Why?

- Do you think Shackleton is a good leader? Why do you think as you do?

Theme 5: Voyagers

Whatever It Takes

Heroism and Courage

With a partner, list ways that Shackleton and his crew showed great courage. Also list examples of brave people you know from your own lives. Then get together in a group to share your ideas and to discuss what makes a hero. Use the following questions for help:

- Do you think Shackleton and his crew are heroes? Why?

- Must you do something daring, like traveling to Antarctica, to show how brave you are? Can someone be a hero in his or her everyday life? If so, how?

Theme 5: Voyagers

    Assignment Cards

Reading Routines

Before You Read . . .

- Read the title and the introduction. Look at the illustrations. What do you think the story will be about?

As You Read . . .

- Pause to evaluate whether the author makes Pepita and her problem seem real.

- Complete your Problem-Solving Chart on **Practice Book** page 168.

- Think of questions you can discuss with your classmates.

Theme 6: Smart Solutions

Assignment Card 1   Pepita Talks Twice

Picture This!

Word Choice

On page 312, words such as *slipped*, *tiptoed*, and *hurried* help the reader picture Pepita on the day that she announces her decision to never speak Spanish again. Where else in the story does the author's word choice help you picture what is happening? As you look back through the story, make a list of the vivid verbs that you find.

Theme 6: Smart Solutions

Literature Discussion

Form a small group with several other classmates. Discuss the following questions and any other questions or ideas you thought of while reading.

- How do you think Pepita's family feels when she stops speaking Spanish?

- Do you think Pepita's decision to stop speaking Spanish is a good one? Explain why you feel this way.

- What are some other ways Pepita might solve her problem?

Theme 6: Smart Solutions

Searching for Clues

Foreshadowing

When a writer gives clues about what will happen later in a story, it is called **foreshadowing**. For example, on page 306 Pepita wants to get home first to teach Lobo to fetch. On page 314, Lobo gets out of the yard and follows Pepita to school. Both of these events foreshadow Lobo chasing the ball into the street on page 328.

Look through the story to find other examples of foreshadowing. What clues are there that Lobo will not listen to Pepita on page 328? What hints did the author give earlier in the story that Lobo would not listen to Pepita when she spoke English? Write your ideas on a piece of paper.

Theme 6: Smart Solutions

Reading Routines

Before You Read . . .

- Read the title and the introduction. Look at the illustrations. What do you think will happen in the story?

As You Read . . .

- Stop to make predictions about what will happen. For help, use story clues and information you already know.

- Complete your Conclusions Chart on **Practice Book** page 188.

- Think of questions to discuss with your classmates.

Theme 6: Smart Solutions

Playing with Personality

Character Development

You can learn a lot about a character's personality through the character's words, actions, and thoughts. For example, Poppa cleans, runs errands, and buys groceries. These actions show that Poppa is kind and helpful.

Work with a partner to identify some of George's personality traits based on details from the story. Then discuss whether you think the author was successful in making George seem like a real boy.

Theme 6: Smart Solutions

Literature Discussion

In a small group, discuss your answers to these questions.

- Why do you think the author has George use so many exaggerations and special expressions? Which are your favorites?

- How well does the author succeed in making the characters seem real? Give examples.

- How does the author show the family's warm feelings for each other?

- How is this story similar to other scary stories you've read? How is it different?

Theme 6: Smart Solutions

Funny Business

Humor

An author often uses one or more of the following elements to create humor in a story:

- **Exaggeration** For example, George says he is drowning in "a sea of sloppy wet kisses."

- **Unexpected events** For example, when Poppa holds up his pants, it's a surprise when they only reach to his knees.

Look back through the story for more examples of these types of humor. Discuss your ideas with a partner.

Theme 6: Smart Solutions

Reading Routines

Before You Read . . .

- Read the title and the introduction. Look at the illustrations. Think about what might happen in the story.

As You Read . . .

- Pause to summarize the story events and the characters' feelings.

- Complete the Generalizations Chart on **Practice Book** page 203 by listing details about story characters and settings.

- Think of questions you can discuss after reading.

Theme 6: Smart Solutions

Sunny Sunday

Changing the Mood

Think about how this opening scene might be different if the chapter were called "Sunny Sunday" instead. What would the Quimbys and Picky-picky be doing on a sunny day? How might Ramona feel? How would household objects be different? Use your ideas to rewrite the opening scene.

Theme 6: Smart Solutions

Literature Discussion

With some classmates, discuss these questions and any other questions or ideas you have.

- How does the author show that each member of the Quimby family is in a bad mood?

- If you could give Ramona any advice about how to cope with a rainy Sunday, what would you say?

- Do you think the author understands children? Why or why not?

- Do you think the members of the Quimby family have a good reason to be so crabby? Why or why not?

Theme 6: Smart Solutions

Eating Smart

Health

It's okay to have a special treat once in a while, but the Quimby dinner isn't a meal you should eat everyday. Think about what you know about healthy eating. Plan a more balanced meal for the Quimbys that includes more fruits, vegetables, and grains, and less fat and sugar. Draw a picture of your meal or cut out pictures from magazines to show what foods and drinks the dinner would include. Label each item in your meal.

Theme 6: Smart Solutions

Observation Checklists

Theme 1

Record observations of student progress for those areas important to you.

−   = Beginning Understanding
√   = Developing Understanding
√+ = Proficient

Student Names

Cliff Hanger						
Comprehension Strategy: Predict/Infer						
Comprehension Skill: Cause and Effect						
Information & Study: Graphic Organizers (KWL)						
Structural Analysis: Base Words						
Phonics: Short Vowels *a, e, i*						
Spelling: Short Vowels *a, e, i*						
Vocabulary Skill: ABC Order (to third letter)						
Grammar: What Is a Sentence?						
Writing Skill: Paragraph That Explains						
Listening/Speaking/Viewing: Literature Discussion						
Reading-Writing Workshop						
Personal Narrative						
The Ballad of Mulan						
Comprehension Strategy: Monitor/Clarify						
Comprehension Skill: Making Inferences						
Information & Study: Dictionary/Alphabetical Order						
Structural Analysis: Syllabication						
Phonics: Short Vowels *o, u*						
Spelling: Short Vowels *o, u*						
Vocabulary Skill: Multiple-Meaning Words						
Grammar: Kinds of Sentences						
Writing Skill: Response Journal Entry						
Listening/Speaking/Viewing: Introductions						

Record observations of student progress for those areas important to you.

− = Beginning Understanding
√ = Developing Understanding
√+ = Proficient

The Lost and Found	Student Names					
Comprehension Strategy: Summarize						
Comprehension Skill: Sequence of Events						
Information & Study: Parts of a Book						
Structural Analysis: Inflected Endings -ed, -ing						
Phonics: Vowel-Consonant-e						
Spelling: Vowel-Consonant-e						
Vocabulary Skill: Parts of a Dictionary						
Grammar: Subjects and Predicates						
Writing Skill: Friendly Letter						
Listening/Speaking/Viewing: Tell a Story						

General Observation						
Independent Reading						
Independent Writing						
Work Habits						

Theme 2

Record observations of student progress for those areas important to you.

− = Beginning Understanding
√ = Developing Understanding
√+ = Proficient

Student Names

The Keeping Quilt							
Comprehension Strategy: Evaluate							
Comprehension Skill: Author's Viewpoint							
Information & Study: Using the Library							
Structural Analysis: Compound Words							
Phonics: Long Vowels *ai, ay, ee, ea*							
Spelling: Long Vowels *ai, ay, ee, ea*							
Vocabulary Skill: Word Families							
Grammar: Common Nouns							
Writing Skill: Paragraph That Compares							
Listening/Speaking/Viewing: Directions							

Reading-Writing Workshop							
Instructions/Explanation							

Grandma's Records							
Comprehension Strategy: Question							
Comprehension Skill: Categorize and Classify							
Information & Study: Conduct an Interview							
Structural Analysis: Plurals: add -*s*; change *y* to *i*							
Phonics: Long *o* Sound							
Spelling: Long *o* Sound							
Vocabulary Skill: Guide Words							
Grammar: Proper Nouns							
Writing Skill: Character Sketch							
Listening/Speaking/Viewing: Telephone Skills							

Observation Checklist

Student Names

Record observations of student progress for those areas important to you.

– = Beginning Understanding
√ = Developing Understanding
√+ = Proficient

The Talking Cloth

Comprehension Strategy: Summarize							
Comprehension Skill: Noting Details							
Information & Study: Taking Notes							
Structural Analysis: Contractions: *'s, n't, 're, 'll*							
Phonics: 3-Letter Clusters; Unexpected Patterns							
Spelling: 3-Letter Clusters; Unexpected Patterns							
Vocabulary Skill: Rhyming Words							
Grammar: Singular and Plural Nouns							
Writing Skill: Answer to a Question							
Listening/Speaking/Viewing: View for Information							

Dancing Rainbows

Comprehension Strategy: Monitor/Clarify							
Comprehension Skill: Topic, Main Idea, Details							
Information & Study: Outlining							
Structural Analysis: Plurals *ch, sh, x, s*							
Phonics: Long *i* Sound *i, ie, igh*							
Spelling: Long *i* Sound *i, ie, igh*							
Vocabulary Skill: Definitions							
Grammar: Special Plural Nouns							
Writing Skill: Newspaper Article							
Listening/Speaking/Viewing: Explain a Process							

General Observation

Independent Reading							
Independent Writing							
Work Habits							

Theme 3

Student Names

Record observations of student progress for those areas important to you.

− = Beginning Understanding
√ = Developing Understanding
√+ = Proficient

Dogzilla							
Comprehension Strategy: Evaluate							
Comprehension Skill: Fantasy and Realism							
Information & Study: Newspapers/Magazines							
Structural Analysis: Plurals: change -f, -fe to -ves							
Phonics: Vowel Sounds in *clown* and *lawn*							
Spelling: Vowel Sounds in *clown* and *lawn*							
Vocabulary Skill: Using Context							
Grammar: Possessive Nouns							
Writing Skill: Journal Entry							
Listening/Speaking/Viewing: Illustrations							

Reading-Writing Workshop							
Story							

The Mysterious Giant of Barletta							
Comprehension Strategy: Question							
Comprehension Skill: Following Directions							
Information & Study: Maps/Atlas							
Structural Analysis: Suffixes -er, -est							
Phonics: Vowel plus *r* Sounds							
Spelling: Vowel plus *r* Sounds							
Vocabulary Skill: Choosing the Correct Meaning							
Grammar: What Is a Verb?							
Writing Skill: Thank-You Note							
Listening/Speaking/Viewing: Reader's Theater							

Student Names

Record observations of student progress for those areas important to you.

− = Beginning Understanding
√ = Developing Understanding
√+ = Proficient

Raising Dragons

Comprehension Strategy: Predict/Infer							
Comprehension Skill: Drawing Conclusions							
Information & Study: Using the Encyclopedia							
Structural Analysis: Suffixes -y, -ly							
Phonics: Sounds j, k, kw							
Spelling: Sounds j, k, kw							
Vocabulary Skill: Pronunciation Key							
Grammar: Present Tense							
Writing Skill: Opinion Paragraph							
Listening/Speaking/Viewing: Conversations							

The Garden of Abdul Gasazi

Comprehension Strategy: Monitor/Clarify							
Comprehension Skill: Story Structure							
Information & Study: Charts, Tables, Graphs							
Structural Analysis: Prefixes un-, dis-, non-							
Phonics: Homophones							
Spelling: Homophones							
Vocabulary Skill: Using a Thesaurus							
Grammar: Past Tense; Future Tense							
Writing Skill: Audio Script							
Listening/Speaking/Viewing: Debates							

General Observation

Independent Reading							
Independent Writing							
Work Habits							

Theme 4

Record observations of student progress for those areas important to you.

− = Beginning Understanding
√ = Developing Understanding
√+ = Proficient

Student Names

Nights of the Pufflings

Comprehension Strategy: Evaluate						
Comprehension Skill: Fact and Opinion						
Information & Study: Multimedia Resources						
Structural Analysis: Syllabication and Review						
Phonics: Vowel plus *r* Sounds in *hair*						
Spelling: Vowel plus *r* Sounds in *hair*						
Vocabulary Skill: Parts of Speech						
Grammar: Verb *to be*						
Writing Skill: Taking Notes						
Listening/Speaking/Viewing: Literature Discussions						

Reading-Writing Workshop

Research Report						

Seal Surfer

Comprehension Strategy: Summarize						
Comprehension Skill: Compare and Contrast						
Information & Study: Skim and Scan						
Structural Analysis: Word Endings *-ed, -ing*						
Phonics: Consonant Clusters *scr, gr, tw, fl, sk*						
Spelling: Word Endings *-ed, -ing*						
Vocabulary Skill: More Multiple-Meaning Words						
Grammar: Helping Verbs						
Writing Skill: News Article						
Listening/Speaking/Viewing: Evaluate Media						

Observation Checklist

Record observations of student progress for those areas important to you.

– = Beginning Understanding
√ = Developing Understanding
√+ = Proficient

Student Names

Two Days in May

Comprehension Strategy: Monitor/Clarify						
Comprehension Skill: Making Judgments						
Information & Study: Adjusting Rate of Reading						
Structural Analysis: Prefixes *un-, re-;* Suffixes *-ful, -ly, -er*						
Phonics: Digraphs *ch, sh, th, tch, wh, wr*						
Spelling: Prefixes *un-, re-;* Suffixes *-ful, -ly, -er*						
Vocabulary Skill: Base Words and Inflected Forms						
Grammar: Using the Correct Verb Form						
Writing Skill: Solving a Problem						
Listening/Speaking/Viewing: Announcements						

General Observation

Independent Reading						
Independent Writing						
Work Habits						

Theme 5

Record observations of student progress for those areas important to you.

– = Beginning Understanding
√ = Developing Understanding
√+ = Proficient

Student Names

Across the Wide Dark Sea

Comprehension Strategy: Question							
Comprehension Skill: Making Inferences							
Information & Study: Multimedia Report							
Structural Analysis: Suffixes *-less, -ness*							
Phonics: Vowel Sounds in *tooth* and *cook*							
Spelling: Vowel Sounds in *tooth* and *cook*							
Vocabulary Skill: Syllables							
Grammar: Subject Pronouns							
Writing Skill: Writing a Play							
Listening/Speaking/Viewing: Oral Reports							

Reading-Writing Workshop

Description							

Yunmi and Halmoni's Trip

Comprehension Strategy: Predict/Infer							
Comprehension Skill: Predicting Outcomes							
Information & Study: Using Graphic Organizers (SQRR)							
Structural Analysis: Possessives, including *s'*							
Phonics: Vowel Sound in *bought*							
Spelling: Vowel Sound in *bought*							
Vocabulary Skill: Analogies							
Grammar: Object Pronouns							
Writing Skill: Taking Messages							
Listening/Speaking/Viewing: Nonverbal Communication							

Record observations of student progress for those areas important to you.

– = Beginning Understanding
√ = Developing Understanding
√+ = Proficient

Student Names

Trapped by the Ice!

Comprehension Strategy: Monitor/Clarify							
Comprehension Skill: Text Organization							
Information & Study: Time Lines/Schedules							
Structural Analysis: VCCV Pattern							
Phonics: Double Consonants							
Spelling: VCCV Pattern							
Vocabulary Skill: Homophones							
Grammar: Possessive Pronouns							
Writing Skill: Learning-Log Entry							
Listening/Speaking/Viewing: Group Problem Solving							

General Observation

Independent Reading							
Independent Writing							
Work Habits							

Theme 6

Record observations of student progress for those areas important to you.

− = Beginning Understanding
√ = Developing Understanding
√+ = Proficient

Student Names

Pepita Talks Twice

Comprehension Strategy: Evaluate							
Comprehension Skill: Problem Solving							
Information & Study: Bilingual Dictionary							
Structural Analysis: VCCCV Pattern							
Phonics: Word Endings *er* or *le*							
Spelling: Word Endings *er* or *le*							
Vocabulary Skill: Synonyms							
Grammar: Adjectives (including *a, an, the*)							
Writing Skill: Writing an Announcement							
Listening/Speaking/Viewing: Resolve Conflicts							

Reading-Writing Workshop

Persuasive Essay							

Poppa's New Pants

Comprehension Strategy: Predict/Infer							
Comprehension Skill: Drawing Conclusions							
Information & Study: Following Directions							
Structural Analysis: VCV Pattern							
Phonics: Word Beginnings *a* or *be*							
Spelling: Word Beginnings *a* or *be*							
Vocabulary Skill: Antonyms							
Grammar: Comparing with Adjectives							
Writing Skill: Summary							
Listening/Speaking/Viewing: Speak to Persuade							

Record observations of student progress for those areas important to you.

−　= Beginning Understanding
√　= Developing Understanding
√+ = Proficient

Student Names						
Ramona Quimby, Age 8						
Comprehension Strategy: Summarize						
Comprehension Skill: Making Generalizations						
Information & Study: Real-Life Reading						
Structural Analysis: Contractions n't, 're, 's, 'll, 'd						
Phonics: Soft c and Soft g						
Spelling: Contractions n't, 're, 's, 'll, 'd						
Vocabulary Skill: Spelling Table						
Grammar: Adverbs						
Writing Skill: Essay						
Listening/Speaking/Viewing: Dramatize a Story						

General Observation						
Independent Reading						
Independent Writing						
Work Habits						

Selection Tests

Name: _____

Name: _____

Cliff Hanger

Write your answers to these questions. Look back at the selection for help.

1. **Strategy Focus: Predict/Infer** What clues might help you predict that Axel will rescue Grits?

   _____

   _____

   _____

   _____

2. Is Dag concerned about Axel climbing the mountain during a storm? Explain how you know.

   _____

   _____

   _____

   _____

Choose the best answer and fill in the circle.

3. How does Dag tell how far away the storm is?
   - ○ **a.** by how black the clouds are
   - ○ **b.** by listening to a weather report
   - ○ **c.** by counting the seconds between the lightning and thunder.
   - ○ **d.** by noting how hard the wind is blowing

Test Continues ➡

Cliff Hanger (continued)

4. Why did Axel free climb the rest of the way down the mountain?

- ○ **a.** It was easier for him to go down.
- ○ **b.** He was too tired to use a rope.
- ○ **c.** He was following his dad's instructions.
- ○ **d.** He used the rest of his rope lowering Grits down the cliff.

Read the sentence and choose the correct answer.

5. They <u>trekked</u> steadily up the wooded trail.

What does the word *trekked* mean?

- ○ **a.** hiked slowly over difficult ground
- ○ **b.** moved very fast
- ○ **c.** drove a car
- ○ **d.** went after

6. The dog was sitting on the <u>ledge</u> high above the ground.

What is a ledge?

- ○ **a.** a foothold
- ○ **b.** a large boulder
- ○ **c.** a shelf of rock
- ○ **d.** a mountain

The Ballad of Mulan

Write your answers to these questions. Look back at the selection for help.

1. **Strategy Focus: Monitor/Clarify** Look back at page 61 of the selection. Why is Mulan worried when she sees her father's name on the scrolls?

   _____

   _____

   _____

2. What does Mulan do when she finally returns to her home? Why do you think she does these things right away?

   _____

   _____

   _____

Choose the best answer and fill in the circle.

3. What does Mulan have to do before going off to war?
   - ○ **a.** ride thousands of miles
   - ○ **b.** meet with the Emperor
   - ○ **c.** buy a horse, a saddle, and a bridle
   - ○ **d.** weave a rug

Test Continues ➡

The Ballad of Mulan (continued)

4. While she's away, Mulan thinks she hears her mother's voice, and she wants to hear her father's. What does this show about Mulan?
   - ○ **a.** She feels tired.
   - ○ **b.** She feels confused.
   - ○ **c.** She feels excited.
   - ○ **d.** She feels homesick.

Read the sentence and choose the correct answer.

5. *After ten years, she returned as a great general, <u>triumphant</u> and victorious!*

   What does the word *triumphant* mean?
   - ○ **a.** successful
   - ○ **b.** boring
   - ○ **c.** loud
   - ○ **d.** laughing

6. Mulan told her parents about all the difficult things she had <u>endured</u>.

   What does the word *endured* mean?
   - ○ **a.** enjoyed
   - ○ **b.** suffered
   - ○ **c.** planned
   - ○ **d.** learned

The Lost and Found

Write your answers to these questions. Look back at the selection for help.

1. **Strategy Focus: Summarize** Tell why Wendell and Floyd say that they have no luck at the beginning of the story.

_____

_____

_____

_____

2. Tell what happens at the end of the story to make the children feel that their luck is changing. List the events in the order they happen.

_____

_____

_____

_____

Choose the best answer and fill in the circle.

3. What do the children do just after they paddle across the river?
   ○ **a.** They go into a tunnel that leads to a winding hallway.
   ○ **b.** They find a sign that says *Hat Room*.
   ○ **c.** They look at a suit of armor.
   ○ **d.** They skip their math test.

Test Continues ➡

The Lost and Found (continued)

4. Which of these events tells you that the story is a fantasy?

○ **a.** Mona loses her lucky hat.

○ **b.** The children find a deep lake in the Lost and Found bin.

○ **c.** The children take a shortcut to get home.

○ **d.** The teacher gets angry.

Read the sentence and choose the correct answer.

5. *Mona leaned farther and farther into the bin. Soon only her feet were* <u>visible</u>.

What does the word *visible* mean?

○ **a.** covered

○ **b.** touching

○ **c.** showing

○ **d.** hidden

6. The lost and found bin was full of <u>wrinkled</u> clothes.

Which word means almost the same thing as *wrinkled*?

○ **a.** situations

○ **b.** rumpled

○ **c.** worried

○ **d.** clean

The Keeping Quilt

Write your answers to these questions. Look back at the selection for help.

1. **Strategy Focus: Evaluate** Did you like the way the author explains how her family traditions have been passed along over the years? Why or why not?

   _____

   _____

   _____

2. Why is the quilt important to the author?

   _____

   _____

   _____

Choose the best answer and fill in the circle.

3. Why does Anna's mother want to make a special quilt?
   - ○ **a.** to have something to pass on to her grandchildren
   - ○ **b.** so she can spend more time with the neighbor ladies
   - ○ **c.** to help her family remember loved ones still in Russia
   - ○ **d.** because she must use up all the old clothes in her basket

Test Continues ➡

The Keeping Quilt (continued)

4. How does the author feel about her family?

  ○ **a.** She believes they should forget the past.

  ○ **b.** She thinks they are very special.

  ○ **c.** She hopes they move back to Russia.

  ○ **d.** She does <u>not</u> want to share their story.

Read the sentence and choose the correct answer.

5. *They cut out animals and flowers from the <u>scraps</u> of clothing.*

What does the word *scraps* mean?

  ○ **a.** bundles

  ○ **b.** threads

  ○ **c.** buttons

  ○ **d.** bits

6. Anna's mother sewed a long thin strip of cloth around the outside of the quilt to make a <u>border</u>.

What is a border?

  ○ **a.** edge

  ○ **b.** center

  ○ **c.** stuffing

  ○ **d.** shape

Grandma's Records

Write your answers to these questions. Look back at the selection for help.

1. **Strategy Focus: Question** What are two questions you might ask to find out about Grandma's hometown?

   _____

   _____

   _____

2. Name two ways Grandma keeps her family traditions alive.

   _____

   _____

   _____

Choose the best answer and fill in the circle.

3. Where are you most likely to see the following: musicians, an audience, singers?

   ○ **a.** in a blizzard

   ○ **b.** in a large theater

   ○ **c.** on a subway in the Bronx

   ○ **d.** in an art studio

Test Continues ➡

Grandma's Records (continued)

4. How does Eric feel about his grandma's music?

- ○ **a.** He thinks it is old-fashioned.
- ○ **b.** He enjoys listening to it with her.
- ○ **c.** He prefers to play outside with other kids.
- ○ **d.** He'd rather listen to his own music.

Read the sentence and choose the correct answer.

5. Eric and Grandma listen to her <u>records</u>.

What is a record?

- ○ **a.** a big radio
- ○ **b.** a pretty song
- ○ **c.** a disk that plays music
- ○ **d.** a loud horn

6. Sammy was <u>performing</u> in New York City.

What does Sammy do when he is performing?

- ○ **a.** He is putting on a show.
- ○ **b.** He is paying a visit to Grandma.
- ○ **c.** He is driving a car.
- ○ **d.** He is telling a story.

The Talking Cloth

Write your answers to these questions. Look back at the selection for help.

1. **Strategy Focus: Summarize** Summarize how Amber comes to learn the ways that adinkra cloth talks.

   _____

   _____

   _____

2. What does adinkra cloth look like?

   _____

   _____

   _____

Choose the best answer and fill in the circle.

3. What does the color of the adinkra cloth stand for?
   - ○ **a.** It names the person who sewed the cloth.
   - ○ **b.** It tells how the wearer feels.
   - ○ **c.** It is a sign that its wearer is not a king.
   - ○ **d.** It shows how warm or cold it is.

Test Continues ➡

The Talking Cloth (continued)

4. Which does *not* belong on a list that tells the meanings of the small black shapes on the cloth?

   ○ **a.** faith

   ○ **b.** power

   ○ **c.** love

   ○ **d.** smiles

Read the sentence and choose the correct answer.

5. *Aunt Phoebe tells the meaning of some <u>symbols</u> on her cloth.*

   What does the word *symbols* mean?

   ○ **a.** stitches made with silk thread

   ○ **b.** brightly colored pictures

   ○ **c.** shapes that stand for ideas

   ○ **d.** black and white photos

6. They used their <u>wealth</u> to give homeless people food and clothing.

   What is wealth?

   ○ **a.** riches

   ○ **b.** tools

   ○ **c.** plan

   ○ **d.** ideas

Dancing Rainbows

Write your answers to these questions. Look back at the selection for help.

1. **Strategy Focus: Monitor/Clarify** Look at the last paragraph on page 249. What does Andy mean by saying that *"a Tewa never dances for himself"*?

   _____

   _____

   _____

2. Write a sentence that tells the main idea of the first paragraph on page 241.

   _____

   _____

   _____

Choose the best answer and fill in the circle.

3. Look at page 247. What one idea best describes these details from that page: the heartbeat of Mother Earth; the drummers' hands; powerful drumbeats; and songs the drummers sing?

   ○ **a.** how Tewa drums are made

   ○ **b.** why Tewa drummers are important

   ○ **c.** why the dancers wear bells on their costumes

   ○ **d.** different Tewa dances

Test Continues ➡

Dancing Rainbows (continued)

4. How are the Eagle dancers' movements like those of real eagles?

- ○ **a.** They keep time to the beat of the drum.
- ○ **b.** They fly to the clouds.
- ○ **c.** They swoop, soar, and circle.
- ○ **d.** They rest between dances.

Read the sentence and choose the correct answer.

5. *Tewas show their <u>respect</u> for all animals with the Buffalo Dance.*

What does it mean to show respect for something?

- ○ **a.** give great honor to
- ○ **b.** feel very worried
- ○ **c.** wish for special gifts
- ○ **d.** ask for joy and happiness

6. The people from Andy's <u>family who lived long ago</u> also danced these Tewa prayers.

Which word below names the people from Andy's family who lived long ago?

- ○ **a.** grandchildren
- ○ **b.** ancestors
- ○ **c.** old enemies
- ○ **d.** neighbors

Dogzilla

Write your answers to these questions. Look back at the selection for help.

1. **Strategy Focus: Evaluate** Do you like the way the author uses real animals in this fantasy story? Explain why or why not.

   _____

   _____

   _____

2. Describe three things that the mice in the story do that show the story is a fantasy.

   _____

   _____

   _____

Choose the best answer and fill in the circle.

3. Which story event below could be part of a realistic story?

   ○ **a.** a dog comes out of a volcano

   ○ **b.** a dog chases cars

   ○ **c.** a dog breathes fire

   ○ **d.** a dog chews a furniture store

Test Continues ➡

Dogzilla (continued)

4. Why does the professor think that teaching Dogzilla to help the community will not solve the mice's problem?

   ○ **a.** She thinks Dogzilla is too old to learn something new.

   ○ **b.** She thinks Dogzilla will brag about what she did.

   ○ **c.** She thinks Dogzilla does not speak their language.

   ○ **d.** She thinks Dogzilla is too dirty.

Read the sentence and choose the best answer.

5. *Suddenly, a blast of warm, sudsy water hit Dogzilla with* <u>*tremendous*</u> *force.*

   What does the word *tremendous* mean?

   ○ **a.** soggy

   ○ **b.** soapy

   ○ **c.** gentle

   ○ **d.** powerful

6. The <u>heroic</u> mice attacked the huge and dangerous dog.

   What does the word *heroic* mean?

   ○ **a.** angry

   ○ **b.** brave

   ○ **c.** weak

   ○ **d.** sneaky

The Mysterious Giant of Barletta

Write your answers to these questions. Look back at the selection for help.

1. **Strategy Focus: Question** Look at page 343. What are three questions about the town of Barletta that you could find answers for on this page?

   _____

   _____

   _____

2. How do you know that the people of Barletta did not have any enemies before the soldiers came?

   _____

   _____

   _____

Choose the best answer and fill in the circle.

3. Which event below shows that the story is a fantasy?
   ○ **a.** Zia Concetta cuts a large onion in two.
   ○ **b.** The soldiers decide to attack Barletta.
   ○ **c.** The townspeople run through the streets in a panic.
   ○ **d.** The giant gets down from his pedestal.

Test Continues ➡

The Mysterious Giant of Barletta (continued)

4. The captain's directions are "About-face! Double time — march!"
   What does he want his soldiers to do?

   ○ **a.** draw their swords and march in two lines

   ○ **b.** turn around and march quickly away

   ○ **c.** hide their faces and sneak past the giant

   ○ **d.** face him and take small steps forward

Read the sentence and choose the best answer.

5. No one knew where the mysterious giant had come from.

   What does the word *mysterious* mean?

   ○ **a.** hard to talk about

   ○ **b.** hard to explain

   ○ **c.** hard to see

   ○ **d.** hard to remember

6. The giant says that the other boys call him a weakling.

   What is a *weakling*?

   ○ **a.** someone who likes to play

   ○ **b.** someone who is not tall

   ○ **c.** someone who is not strong

   ○ **d.** someone who is friendly

Raising Dragons

Write your answers to these questions. Look back at the selection for help.

1. **Strategy Focus: Predict/Infer** Look at page 369. What clues help you predict that the girl and her father have found a dragon's egg?

   _____

   _____

   _____

2. What changes because Hank saves the tomatoes from drying out?

   _____

   _____

   _____

Choose the best answer and fill in the circle.

3. Why does Hank try to control his temper when the little girl is around?
   - ○ **a.** He doesn't want his fiery breath to hurt her.
   - ○ **b.** He is afraid she won't like him anymore.
   - ○ **c.** He is ashamed of his temper.
   - ○ **d.** He thinks she will laugh at him.

4. Why does the little girl take Hank to the dragons' island?
   - ○ **a.** Her parents are afraid of Hank.
   - ○ **b.** He is too big to fit in the barn.
   - ○ **c.** She wants to get him away from the curious crowds.
   - ○ **d.** He eats so much that they can't feed him anymore.

Test Continues ➡

Raising Dragons (continued)

Read the sentence and choose the best answer.

5. *One morning with Samson, our mule, <u>hitched</u> for work, Pa set out to plow the fields.*

   What does the word *hitched* mean?

   ○ **a.** too tired

   ○ **b.** brushed and fed

   ○ **c.** strong and healthy

   ○ **d.** fastened to a plow

6. We planted seeds and then we <u>tended</u> the crops every day.

   What does the word *tended* mean?

   ○ **a.** set fire to

   ○ **b.** took care of

   ○ **c.** put bugs on

   ○ **d.** picked the fruit of

The Garden of Abdul Gasazi

1. **Strategy Focus: Monitor/Clarify** Look at pages 406–410. What seems to have happened to Fritz?

   _____

   _____

   _____

2. What is Alan's problem in this story?

   _____

   _____

   _____

Choose the best answer and fill in the circle.

3. What does the beginning of the story tell you about Fritz?
   - ○ **a.** He is really a duck.
   - ○ **b.** He goes to Abdul Gasazi's garden every day.
   - ○ **c.** He adores Miss Hester.
   - ○ **d.** He bites and misbehaves.

4. As he walks toward Miss Hester's house, how does Alan know that Miss Hester is home?
   - ○ **a.** She calls out to him.
   - ○ **b.** He sees her car in the driveway.
   - ○ **c.** He sees the lights on in the house.
   - ○ **d.** He smells dinner cooking.

Test Continues ➡

The Garden of Abdul Gasazi (continued)

Read the sentence and choose the best answer.

5. *Alan nervously climbed the great stairs,* <u>convinced</u> *Fritz had come this way and been captured.*

What does the word *convinced* mean?

- ○ **a.** believing
- ○ **b.** doubting
- ○ **c.** pretending
- ○ **d.** wishing

6. Some <u>incredible</u> things happen to Alan in Mr. Gasazi's garden.

What does the word *incredible* mean?

- ○ **a.** interesting
- ○ **b.** hard to believe
- ○ **c.** fun and exciting
- ○ **d.** very colorful

Nights of the Pufflings

Write your answers to these questions. Look back at the selection for help.

1. **Strategy Focus: Evaluate** Which part of the nights of the pufflings do you think the author describes best? What does the author do to help you understand what happens and how the scene looks?

_____

_____

_____

_____

2. Tell one fact about how the Icelanders help the pufflings.

_____

_____

_____

_____

Choose the best answer and fill in the circle.

3. Which statement below is an opinion about puffins?

   ○ **a.** Puffins come ashore once a year.

   ○ **b.** Puffins nest in burrows.

   ○ **c.** Puffins eat fish.

   ○ **d.** Puffins are beautiful and special birds.

Test Continues ➡

Nights of the Pufflings (continued)

4. People sometimes cause problems for wildlife.

   Which detail from the selection supports this main idea?

   ○ **a.** The children rescue the pufflings and set them free near the ocean.

   ○ **b.** The village lights cause some pufflings to get confused and land in the village.

   ○ **c.** The children sleep late in the day so they can stay out at night.

   ○ **d.** The adult puffins take fish to their babies.

Read the sentence and choose the best answer.

5. *The pufflings are ready to fly and will at last <u>venture</u> out into the night.*

   What does the word *venture* mean?

   ○ **a.** try to hide

   ○ **b.** peek

   ○ **c.** dare to go

   ○ **d.** swim

6. We couldn't find people anywhere so we decided the town was <u>uninhabited</u>.

   What does the word *uninhabited* mean?

   ○ **a.** asleep

   ○ **b.** crowded

   ○ **c.** busy

   ○ **d.** empty

Seal Surfer

Write your answers to these questions. Look back at the selection for help.

1. **Strategy Focus: Summarize** Summarize what happens on the day that the seal helps Ben out of danger.

   _____

   _____

   _____

   _____

2. In what ways are Ben and his granddad similar to the seal pup and her mother?

   _____

   _____

   _____

   _____

Choose the best answer and fill in the circle.

3. Which of the following events happens first?
   ○ **a.** The seals listen to music with Ben and Granddad.
   ○ **b.** The seal pup learns to swim.
   ○ **c.** Ben brings his own grandchildren to watch the seals.
   ○ **d.** The seal pup saves Ben's life.

Test Continues ➡

Seal Surfer (continued)

4. How are Ben and the seal pup alike?

○ **a.** They are the same age.

○ **b.** They both love to surf and play in the waves.

○ **c.** They both use surfboards to surf.

○ **d.** They both stay close to their mother.

Read the sentence and choose the best answer.

5. The seals <u>basked</u> happily in the sun.

What did the seals do?

○ **a.** ate in the sun

○ **b.** played in the sun

○ **c.** swam in the sun

○ **d.** lay in the sun

6. Ben liked to <u>surf</u> the waves with the young seal.

Which word means almost the same as the underlined word?

○ **a.** ride

○ **b.** splash

○ **c.** dodge

○ **d.** watch

Two Days in May

Write your answers to these questions. Look back at the selection for help.

1. **Strategy Focus: Monitor/Clarify** Look at pages 73–75. Why is Sonia so surprised to see deer in her garden?

   _____

   _____

   _____

   _____

2. Do you think the people in Sonia's neighborhood come up with a good plan to save the deer? Why or why not?

   _____

   _____

   _____

   _____

Choose the best answer and fill in the circle.

3. How does the animal control officer help solve the deer problem?
   - ○ **a.** He leads the deer back to the woods.
   - ○ **b.** He calls his boss and refuses to hurt the deer.
   - ○ **c.** He has a truck bring in more food for the deer.
   - ○ **d.** Instead of shooting the deer, he waits for the wildlife rescuer to come.

Test Continues ➡

Two Days in May (continued)

4. What might have happened if Mr. Benny had not been able to get Carl Jackson to rescue the deer?

   ○ **a.** The deer might have lived in the city streets.

   ○ **b.** Sonia's neighbors might have found someone else to take the deer to a good home.

   ○ **c.** The animal control officer might have let the deer stay in Sonia's garden.

   ○ **d.** Sonia might have been angry that the deer ate her lettuce.

Read the sentence and choose the best answer.

5. Sonia looked out into her garden and saw deer <u>eating</u> there.

   Which word means the same as the underlined word?

   ○ **a.** wandering

   ○ **b.** starving

   ○ **c.** grazing

   ○ **d.** surrounding

6. *The city is afraid the deer will <u>starve</u>.*

   Which phrase means the same as the underlined word?

   ○ **a.** not have enough to eat

   ○ **b.** get hit by a car

   ○ **c.** eat too much lettuce

   ○ **d.** be shot by the animal control officer

Across the Wide Dark Sea

Write your answers to these questions. Look back at the selection for help.

1. **Strategy Focus: Question** List some questions you can ask about the story to help a reader understand what was difficult about the Pilgrims' journey on the ship.

   _____

   _____

   _____

   _____

2. At the end of the story, why do you think the boy's father tells him to look at the settlement as the ship sails away?

   _____

   _____

   _____

   _____

Choose the best answer and fill in the circle.

3. Which of these settings is not included in the story?

   ○ **a.** the Pilgrims' ship

   ○ **b.** the settlement built by the Pilgrims

   ○ **c.** the wild, new land

   ○ **d.** the village where the Indians live

Test Continues ➡

Across the Wide Dark Sea (continued)

4. How do you think the boy feels when he watches the ship sail back to his old home?

   ○ **a.** He is happy that he never has to go back to his old home.

   ○ **b.** He is upset because he wants to take another trip on the boat.

   ○ **c.** He is sad to see the ship go and scared to be left behind in the new land.

   ○ **d.** He is angry because he doesn't like it in the new land and wants to leave too.

Read the sentence and choose the best answer.

5. The Pilgrims were <u>weary</u> after their long journey.

   What does the word *weary* mean?

   ○ **a.** excited

   ○ **b.** tired

   ○ **c.** nervous

   ○ **d.** fighting

6. *There was nothing to do but eat our meals of salt pork, beans, and bread, tidy up our <u>cramped</u> space, sleep when we could, and try to keep dry.*

   What does the word *cramped* mean?

   ○ **a.** dark

   ○ **b.** lonely

   ○ **c.** crowded

   ○ **d.** open

Yunmi and Halmoni's Trip

Write your answers to these questions. Look back at the selection for help.

1. **Strategy Focus: Predict/Infer** What clues in the story might help a reader predict that Yunmi is going to feel left out when she and Halmoni are in Korea?

   _____

   _____

   _____

   _____

2. What do you think might happen when Yunmi asks her cousins to visit her in New York? What kinds of things might they do there?

   _____

   _____

   _____

   _____

Choose the best answer and fill in the circle.

3. What causes Yunmi to think that Halmoni might not want to go back to New York?
   - ○ **a.** Halmoni tells her that she does not like New York.
   - ○ **b.** Halmoni seems happier and busier with more family around her.
   - ○ **c.** Halmoni buys a house in Korea.
   - ○ **d.** Halmoni wants to be a teacher in Korea.

Test Continues ➡

Yunmi and Halmoni's Trip (continued)

4. Based on this story, which statement below seems true?

○ **a.** Picnics in Korea are always bigger than picnics in New York.

○ **b.** Everyone in Korea and New York likes to go to museums.

○ **c.** All children spend more time with their grandmothers than with their grandfathers.

○ **d.** Some children feel left out when other children are getting more attention.

Read the sentence and choose the best answer.

5. *They sped down broad highways, then through streets crowded with* <u>*skyscrapers*</u>.

What were the streets crowded with?

○ **a.** honking cars

○ **b.** people selling things

○ **c.** very tall buildings

○ **d.** pretty houses

6. The girls paid the street <u>vendor</u> for their cakes.

Which word means the same as the underlined word?

○ **a.** seller

○ **b.** driver

○ **c.** sweeper

○ **d.** guard

Trapped by the Ice!

1. **Strategy Focus: Monitor/Clarify** Look back at page 218.
   Why is Shackleton so concerned about his men?

   _____

   _____

   _____

   _____

2. Where do the headings appear in the selection? What information do
   they give you? How does this information help you understand the
   selection?

   _____

   _____

   _____

   _____

Choose the best answer and fill in the circle.

3. What happens just before Shackleton and his small crew land on
   South Georgia Island?

   ○ **a.** They slide down a mountain.

   ○ **b.** They survive the worst hurricane they have ever had.

   ○ **c.** They are attacked by a sea leopard.

   ○ **d.** A graybeard almost sinks their boat.

Test Continues ➡

Trapped by the Ice! (continued)

4. Shackleton is a hero.

   Which detail from the selection best supports this main idea?

   ○ **a.** Shackleton does not succeed in doing what he sets out to do.

   ○ **b.** Shackleton wants to be the first person to cross the South Pole's ice cap.

   ○ **c.** Shackleton is the leader of the crew.

   ○ **d.** Shackleton returns to Elephant Island, then brings all his men back home alive.

Read the sentence and choose the best answer.

5. *He knew his men could not all survive the* <u>grueling</u> *800-mile open-boat journey to the whaling station.*

   Which phrase below means almost the same as the underlined word?

   ○ **a.** difficult and tiring

   ○ **b.** dangerous and exciting

   ○ **c.** icy and cold

   ○ **d.** wet and crowded

6. Hiking to the whaling station would be a <u>perilous</u> journey, but it was their only chance to survive.

   What does the word *perilous* mean?

   ○ **a.** dull

   ○ **b.** easy

   ○ **c.** dangerous

   ○ **d.** fun

Pepita Talks Twice

Write your answers to these questions. Look back at the selection for help.

1. **Strategy Focus: Evaluate** Does the author do a good job making Pepita seem like a real girl? Give examples from the story.

   _____

   _____

   _____

   _____

2. What new problems occur when Pepita stops speaking Spanish?

   _____

   _____

   _____

Choose the best answer and fill in the circle.

3. Why does Pepita think it is unfair that she has to speak two languages?

   ○ **a.** She is the only one in her family who has to speak Spanish.

   ○ **b.** She does not like singing Spanish songs with her friends.

   ○ **c.** She gets confused when she tries to think of the words.

   ○ **d.** She sometimes misses doing her own things because she is helping others.

Test Continues ➡

Pepita Talks Twice (continued)

4. How do you think the author feels about people speaking two languages?

   ○ **a.** She thinks it is an easy thing to do.

   ○ **b.** She thinks it is a good thing.

   ○ **c.** She thinks it is a waste of time.

   ○ **d.** She thinks it is something only adults should do.

Read the sentence and choose the correct answer.

5. <u>Juan</u> took a <u>bite</u> of his <u>tortilla</u> and asked Pepita why she did not call their dog <u>Lobo</u> anymore.

   Which word below is the name of a food?

   ○ **a.** Juan

   ○ **b.** bite

   ○ **c.** tortilla

   ○ **d.** Lobo

6. *It's a fine thing to know two <u>languages</u>.*

   Which answer choice below gives examples of two languages?

   ○ **a.** tacos and salsa

   ○ **b.** cats and dogs

   ○ **c.** Spanish and English

   ○ **d.** boys and girls

Poppa's New Pants

Write your answers to these questions. Look back at the selection for help.

1. **Strategy Focus: Predict/Infer** Read page 352. What clues help you predict what is really happening when the small, white shape comes into the room?

_____

_____

_____

_____

2. Who are the mysterious nighttime visitors? What do they do?

_____

_____

_____

_____

Choose the best answer and fill in the circle.

3. How are the three "ghosts" different from each other?
   - ○ **a.** One floats, one snips, and one rustles.
   - ○ **b.** One is quiet, one is loud, and one laughs.
   - ○ **c.** One is white, one is gray, and one is invisible.
   - ○ **d.** One is small, one is tall and thin, and one is big.

Test Continues ➡

Poppa's New Pants (continued)

4. What is the result of all three women hemming the pants?

○ **a.** The pants fit George.

○ **b.** Poppa has to throw the pants away.

○ **c.** Poppa can't go to church.

○ **d.** Poppa laughs and wears shorts to church.

Read the sentence and choose the correct answer.

5. He couldn't wear his favorite pants until the hole in the knee was <u>mended</u>.

   What does the word *mended* mean?

○ **a.** finished

○ **b.** bigger

○ **c.** fixed

○ **d.** torn

6. *The <u>fabric</u> was as velvety soft as old Buck's nose.*

   Which word below means the same as *fabric*?

○ **a.** pocket

○ **b.** belt

○ **c.** cloth

○ **d.** button

Selection Tests

Ramona Quimby, Age 8

Write your answers to these questions. Look back at the selection for help.

1. **Strategy Focus: Summarize** What changes the Quimbys' day from a dreary one into a happy one?

   _____

   _____

   _____

   _____

2. What does the story show you about what most families are like?

   _____

   _____

   _____

   _____

Choose the best answer and fill in the circle.

3. What can you tell about Ramona by the way she acts toward the stranger?

   ○ **a.** She talks only to people whose clothes match.

   ○ **b.** She is very polite.

   ○ **c.** She doesn't like to be teased.

   ○ **d.** She thinks everyone should be friendly.

Test Continues ➡

Ramona Quimby, Age 8 (continued)

4. Based on what happens in the story, which statement do you think is true most of the time?

○ **a.** Cats shouldn't go out in the rain.

○ **b.** Parents are more cheerful than children.

○ **c.** Little sisters are messier than big sisters.

○ **d.** Rainy days can affect the way people feel.

Read the sentence and choose the correct answer.

5. *Even lunch, leftovers Mrs. Quimby had wanted to clear out of the refrigerator, had been* dreary.

Which word below means the same as *dreary?*

○ **a.** interesting

○ **b.** sweet

○ **c.** dull

○ **d.** delicious

6. The sound of the terrible rain pelting against the windowpanes made it hard to hear the radio.

What does the word *pelting* mean?

○ **a.** beating

○ **b.** breaking

○ **c.** sliding

○ **d.** twisting

ANSWER KEY

THEME 1

Selection 1

Cliff Hanger

Sample answers provided for questions 1 and 2.

1. Answers will vary, but should include some of the following: When Axel first learns Grits is on the mountain, he becomes upset; Axel doesn't hesitate to go after Grits during a storm; Axel climbs the mountain against his dad's better judgment. *(Strategy Focus: Predict/Infer)* (3 points)

2. He is very worried about Axel. I know this because when Axel sees Grits on the ledge, he starts climbing and Dag takes a deep breath to calm himself. Also, when Axel makes it back down, Dag says, "That was so close, I can't talk about it." *(cause and effect)* (3)

3. **c.** by counting the seconds between the lightning and thunder *(noting details)* (1)

4. **d.** He used the rest of his rope lowering Grits down the cliff. *(cause and effect)* (1)

5. **a.** hiked slowly over difficult ground *(key vocabulary)* (1)

6. **c.** a shelf of rock *(key vocabulary)* (1)

Assessment Tip: Total 10 Points

Selection 2

The Ballad of Mulan

Sample answers provided for questions 1 and 2.

1. Answers will vary, but should include steps such as rereading, asking questions, and reading ahead to understand the story. For example: I don't understand why Mulan is worried about her father's name on the scrolls. When I reread, I know it's about the war. I read ahead and find out that Mulan's father is too old to fight. Now I know that the Emperor wants the men with their names on the scrolls to fight in the war. That's why Mulan is worried. *(Strategy Focus: Monitor/Clarify)* (3 points)

2. Mulan takes off her armor and puts on a dress. She brushes her hair and puts on a flower. I think she does these things because she doesn't want to look and act like a soldier anymore. *(making inferences)* (3)

3. **c.** buy a horse, a saddle, and a bridle *(sequence of events)* (1)

4. **d.** She feels homesick. *(making inferences)* (1)

5. **a.** successful *(key vocabulary)* (1)

6. **b.** suffered *(key vocabulary)* (1)

Assessment Tip: Total 10 Points

Selection 3

The Lost and Found

Sample answers provided for questions 1 and 2.

1. A giant squid made the boys miss a math test. Their teacher is angry at them, and they have been sent to the principal's office. *(Strategy Focus: Summarize)* (3 points)

2. Answers will vary, but should include most of the following events, in the order given here: Mona finds her lucky hat; the children find their way out of the Lost and Found just in time for the boys to meet with the principal; the teacher lets the boys take their math test; Mona, their new friend, waits for them after school, and they all walk home together. *(sequence of events)* (3)

3. **a.** They go into a tunnel that leads to a winding hallway. *(sequence of events)* (1)

4. **b.** The children find a deep lake in the Lost and Found bin. *(fantasy and realism)* (1)

5. **c.** showing *(key vocabulary)* (1)

6. **b.** rumpled *(key vocabulary)* (1)

Assessment Tip: Total 10 Points

ANSWER KEY

THEME 2

Selection 1

The Keeping Quilt

Sample answers provided for questions 1 and 2.

1. Yes; it helps me understand why she likes her family traditions so much. No; the reason for keeping so many traditions isn't explained. *(Strategy Focus: Evaluate)* (3 Points)
2. She knows it's been used at so many family celebrations over the years; it's become a family tradition; it's part of her family's history. *(author's viewpoint)* (3)
3. **c.** to help her family remember loved ones still in Russia *(noting details)* (1)
4. **b.** She thinks they are very special. *(author's viewpoint)* (1)
5. **d.** bits *(key vocabulary)* (1)
6. **a.** edge *(key vocabulary)* (1)

Assessment Tip: Total 10 Points

Selection 2

Grandma's Records

Sample answers provided for questions 1 and 2.

1. Where is Santurce located? Is Santurce a large town? *(Strategy Focus: Question)* (3 Points)
2. She listens to music from Puerto Rico with her grandson; she cooks traditional Spanish food when her nephew comes to visit. *(categorize and classify)* (3)
3. **b.** in a large theater *(categorize and classify)* (1)
4. **b.** He enjoys listening to it with her. *(making inferences)* (1)
5. **c.** a disk that plays music *(key vocabulary)* (1)
6. **a.** He is putting on a show. *(key vocabulary)* (1)

Assessment Tip: Total 10 Points

Selection 3

The Talking Cloth

Sample answers provided for questions 1 and 2.

1. Her Aunt Phoebe tells Amber how people in Ghana use the color of the cloth to show how they feel. The symbols on the cloth have different meanings. *(Strategy Focus: Summarize)* (3 Points)
2. It is a long, colored silk cloth. It has embroidered sections and small, black symbols printed all over it. *(noting details)* (3)
3. **b.** It tells how the wearer feels. *(noting details)* (1)
4. **d.** smiles *(categorize and classify)* (1)
5. **c.** shapes that stand for ideas *(key vocabulary)* (1)
6. **a.** riches *(key vocabulary)* (1)

Assessment Tip: Total 10 Points

Selection 4

Dancing Rainbows

Sample answers provided for questions 1 and 2.

1. He dances for everything and for everybody; he prays for all people and all things. *(Strategy Focus: Monitor/Clarify)* (3 Points)
2. Tewa dances are prayers for the tribe. *(topic, main idea, details)* (3)
3. **b.** why Tewa drummers are important *(topic, main idea, details)* (1)
4. **c.** They swoop, soar, and circle. *(compare/contrast)* (1)
5. **a.** give great honor to *(key vocabulary)* (1)
6. **b.** ancestors *(key vocabulary)* (1)

Assessment Tip: Total 10 Points

ANSWER KEY

THEME 3

Selection 1

Dogzilla

Sample answers provided for questions 1 and 2.

1. Thinking of real animals doing the things in the story make it humorous. Or, cartoon animals would make the story more fun. *(Strategy Focus: Evaluate)* (3 points)
2. Answers could include three of the following: They talk, have a cook-off, have a mouse army, hold a meeting, give a dog a bath, and rebuild their city. *(fantasy and realism)* (3)
3. **b.** a dog chases cars *(fantasy and realism)* (1)
4. **a.** She thinks Dogzilla is too old to learn something new. *(problem solving)* (1)
5. **d.** powerful *(key vocabulary)* (1)
6. **b.** brave *(key vocabulary)* (1)

Assessment Tip: Total 10 Points

Selection 2

The Mysterious Giant of Barletta

Sample answers provided for questions 1 and 2.

1. What do people in Barletta do early in the morning? Why do people go to the market? What kind of birds live in Barletta? *(Strategy Focus: Question)* (3 points)
2. They did not have any soldiers or weapons. *(making inferences)* (3)
3. **d.** The giant gets down from his pedestal. *(fantasy and realism)* (1)
4. **b.** turn around and march quickly away *(following directions)* (1)
5. **b.** hard to explain *(key vocabulary)* (1)
6. **c.** someone who is not strong *(key vocabulary)* (1)

Assessment Tip: Total 10 Points

Selection 3

Raising Dragons

Sample answers provided for questions 1 and 2.

1. They find something that looks like a big rock, but is too round and too smooth and too soft to be a rock. Also, it is too big to be the egg for any bird or reptile that they know. Also, the page begins by saying this is "the day my life with dragons began." *(Strategy Focus: Predict/Infer)* (3 points)
2. Ma's feelings change. She starts to like Hank and begins making him fancy dinners. *(cause and effect)* (3)
3. **a.** He doesn't want his fiery breath to hurt her. *(drawing conclusions)* (1)
4. **c.** She wants to get him away from the curious crowds. *(drawing conclusions)* (1)
5. **d.** fastened to a plow *(key vocabulary)* (1)
6. **b.** took care of *(key vocabulary)* (1)

Assessment Tip: Total 10 Points

Selection 4

The Garden of Abdul Gasazi

Sample answers provided for questions 1 and 2.

1. It seems that Fritz has been turned into a duck, stolen Alan's hat, and then turned back into a dog and returned home with Alan's hat. But it could be that the duck was not Fritz. Fritz could have found Alan's hat after the duck dropped it, and then returned home. *(Strategy Focus: Monitor/Clarify)* (3 points)
2. When Fritz runs away, Alan needs to find him or he will be in trouble. *(story structure)* (3)
3. **d.** He bites and misbehaves. *(story structure)* (1)
4. **c.** He sees the lights on in the house. *(noting details)* (1)
5. **a.** believing *(key vocabulary)* (1)
6. **b.** hard to believe *(key vocabulary)* (1)

Assessment Tip: Total 10 Points

ANSWER KEY

THEME 4

Selection 1

Nights of the Pufflings

Sample answers provided for questions 1 and 2.

1. I think the scene the author describes best is when Halla takes a puffling to the beach to let it go. The author describes what Halla does and what she says. He tells how she holds the puffling, counts to three in her language, and launches it up into the air. *(Strategy Focus: Evaluate)* (3 points)
2. The children put the pufflings into cardboard boxes and carry them to the sea to let them go. *(fact and opinion)* (3)
3. **d.** Puffins are beautiful and special birds. *(fact and opinion)* (1)
4. **b.** The village lights cause some pufflings to get confused and land in the village. *(topic, main idea, supporting details)* (1)
5. **c.** dare to go *(key vocabulary)* (1)
6. **d.** empty *(key vocabulary)* (1)

Assessment Tip: Total 10 Points

Selection 2

Seal Surfer

Sample answers provided for questions 1 and 2.

1. A wave knocks Ben off his surfboard and he hits a rock and starts to sink. The seal pushes him back onto his surfboard. Then a wave carries Ben to shore and his friends make sure he is all right. *(Strategy Focus: Summarize)* (3 points)
2. They take care of each other, like music, and like to spend time together by the sea. The mother seal teaches the young seal to swim and Granddad teaches Ben about fishing and seals. *(compare and contrast)* (3)
3. **b.** The seal pup learns to swim. *(sequence of events)* (1)
4. **b.** They both love to surf and play in the waves. *(compare and contrast)* (1)
5. **d.** lay in the sun *(key vocabulary)* (1)
6. **a.** ride *(key vocabulary)* (1)

Assessment Tip: Total 10 Points

Selection 3

Two Days in May

Sample answers provided for questions 1 and 2.

1. Sonia is surprised because she lives in a big, busy city. The only kinds of animals she sees in her neighborhood are pigeons and squirrels. It is not the kind of place where deer usually like to go. *(Strategy Focus: Monitor/Clarify)* (3 points)
2. Yes, I think it is a good way to save the deer because no people or deer get hurt and everybody gets to know one another better. It only took a day to find a good home for the deer, and they didn't have one before. *(making judgments)* (3)
3. **d.** Instead of shooting the deer, he waits for the wildlife rescuer to come. *(problem solving)* (1)
4. **b.** Sonia's neighbors might have found someone else to take the deer to a good home. *(predicting outcomes)* (1)
5. **c.** grazing *(key vocabulary)* (1)
6. **a.** not have enough to eat *(key vocabulary)* (1)

Assessment Tip: Total 10 Points

ANSWER KEY

THEME 5

Selection 1

Across the Wide Dark Sea

Sample answers provided for questions 1 and 2.

1. What do the people do all day while they are on the ship? What is it like when the seas get rough? What do they worry about on the ship? What dangers do they face on the ship? *(Strategy Focus: Question)* (3 points)
2. He knows the boy feels scared and worried about being left and he wants to remind him that they have made a safe home and are going to be all right. *(making inferences)* (3)
3. **d.** the village where the Indians live *(story structure)* (1)
4. **c.** He is sad to see the ship go and scared to be left behind in the new land. *(making inferences)* (1)
5. **b.** tired *(key vocabulary)* (1)
6. **c.** crowded *(key vocabulary)* (1)

Assessment Tip: Total 10 Points

Selection 2

Yunmi and Halmoni's Trip

Sample answers provided for questions 1 and 2.

1. Halmoni is often gone and when she comes home, Yunmi's cousins sit on Halmoni's lap, talk to her, and get all her attention. Yunmi wishes her cousins would disappear so she and Halmoni can talk again. *(Strategy Focus: Predict/Infer)* (3 points)
2. Yunmi's cousins love Yunmi and Halmoni and will be happy to come visit them in New York. Yunmi and Halmoni might take them sightseeing and shopping, introduce them to friends and family, and have them try different kinds of American food. *(predicting outcomes)* (3)
3. **b.** Halmoni seems happier and busier with more family around her. *(cause and effect)* (1)
4. **d.** Some children feel left out when other children are getting more attention. *(making generalizations)* (1)
5. **c.** very tall buildings *(key vocabulary)* (1)
6. **a.** seller *(key vocabulary)* (1)

Assessment Tip: Total 10 Points

Selection 3

Trapped by the Ice!

Sample answers provided for questions 1 and 2.

1. Shackleton is worried about his men because the *Endurance* is being crushed by the ice. The ship is leaking and breaking apart. Without the ship, the men will be stuck hundreds of miles away from land. They will have no shelter to protect them from the snow, ice, and cold. *(Strategy Focus: Monitor/Clarify)* (3 points)
2. The headings are above the text on some of the pages. They tell what date it is. This tells me the order of the selection events and how much time passes between the events. *(text organization)* (3)
3. **b.** They survive the worst hurricane they have ever had. *(sequence of events)* (1)
4. **d.** Shackleton returns to Elephant Island, then brings all his men back home alive. *(topic, main idea, supporting detail)* (1)
5. **a.** difficult and tiring *(key vocabulary)* (1)
6. **c.** dangerous *(key vocabulary)* (1)

Assessment Tip: Total 10 Points

ANSWER KEY

THEME 6

Selection 1

Pepita Talks Twice

Sample answers provided for questions 1 and 2.

1. I think the author does a good job because Pepita does things a real girl would do. She likes playing with her dog and singing with her friends, but she also argues with her brother and gets frustrated when she can't do the things she wants to do. *(Strategy Focus: Evaluate)* (3 Points)

2. When Pepita stops speaking Spanish, she can no longer do many of the things she enjoys. She can't sing Spanish songs with her friends or ask for her favorite Spanish foods. Also, her dog does not listen to her when she speaks English only. *(problem solving)* (3)

3. **d.** She sometimes misses doing her own things because she is helping others. *(making inferences)* (1)

4. **b.** She thinks it is a good thing. *(author's viewpoint)* (1)

5. **c.** tortilla *(key vocabulary)* (1)

6. **c.** Spanish and English *(key vocabulary)* (1)

Assessment Tip: Total 10 Points

Selection 2

Poppa's New Pants

Sample answers provided for questions 1 and 2.

1. The clues are that the shape was small, the rocking chair creaked, and the snipping and rustling sounds. *(Strategy Focus: Predict/Infer)* (3 Points)

2. Grandma Tiny, Big Mama, and Aunt Viney each come into the kitchen, pick up the pants from the rocking chair, cut them, and hem them. *(drawing conclusions)* (3)

3. **d.** One is small, one is tall and thin, and one is big. *(compare and contrast)* (1)

4. **a.** The pants fit George. *(cause and effect)* (1)

5. **c.** fixed *(key vocabulary)* (1)

6. **c.** cloth *(key vocabulary)* (1)

Assessment Tip: Total 10 Points

Selection 3

Ramona Quimby, Age 8

Sample answers provided for questions 1 and 2.

1. Getting out together and having a stranger be kind to them makes the family start appreciating each other. *(Strategy Focus: Summarize)* (3 Points)

2. Most families love each other even if they do not act nicely all of the time. *(making generalizations)* (3)

3. **c.** She doesn't like to be teased. *(drawing conclusions)* (1)

4. **d.** Rainy days can affect the way people feel. *(making generalizations)* (1)

5. **c.** dull *(key vocabulary)* (1)

6. **a.** beating *(key vocabulary)* (1)

Assessment Tip: Total 10 Points